MW00638186

The MIRACLE MORNING

THE NOT-SO-OBVIOUS SECRET GUARANTEED TO TRANSFORM YOUR LIFE BEFORE 8AM

COMPANION PLANNER

A COMPANION TO THE #1 INTERNATIONAL BESTSELLER

THE MIRACLE MORNING COMPANION PLANNER

Hal Elrod & Natalie Janji
with Honorée Corder

Copyright © 2017 by Hal Elrod. All rights reserved.

Cover Copyright © 2017 by Hal Elrod International, Inc.

No part of this publication may be reproduced or transmitted in any form or by any means, mechanical or electronic, including photocopying and recording, or by any information storage and retrieval systems, without permission in writing from the author or publisher (except by a reviewer, who may quote brief passages and/or show brief video clips in a review).

Disclaimer: The advice and strategies contained herein may not be suitable for every situation. This work is sold with the understanding that the Author and Publisher are not engaged in rendering legal, accounting, or other professional services. Neither the Author nor the Publisher shall be liable for damages arising here from. The fact that an organization or website is referred to in this work as a citation or a potential source of further information does not mean that the Author or the Publisher endorses the information that the organization or website may provide or recommendations it may make. Further, readers should be aware that Internet websites listed in this work may have changed or disappeared between when this work was written and when it is read.

Interior Design: Christina Gorchos, 3CsBooks.com

Paperback ISBN:978-1-942589-21-1
Digital ISBN: 978-1-942589-22-8

This planner belongs to:

_____

If lost please return to:

_____

_____

_____

Contact Information

_____

_____

DEDICATION

HAL

I dedicate this book to The Miracle Morning Community and thank you, from the bottom of my heart, for supporting each other to Elevate the Consciousness of Humanity, One Morning at a Time.

NATALIE

This book is dedicated to my family. To my ancestors that made this possible, thank you. Mom, Dad, and George, I love you and I am forever grateful for each of you. Mom, thank you for your constant love, vibrant energy, and support of my dreams. Dad, thank you for all your hard work over the years and showing me the power in a smile. George, thank you for being the greatest brother, best friend, and supporter I could have ever wished for!

This book is also dedicated to The Miracle Morning™ community, a community that has expanded my definition of "family." I am forever grateful to be a member of The Miracle Morning™ community, and honored to be a contributor to The Miracle Morning™ mission: "Elevating the consciousness of humanity, one morning at a time."

HONOREE

I dedicate this book to my family, for whom I do everything.

INTRODUCTION

In 2012, I published *The Miracle Morning: The Not-So-Obvious Secret Guaranteed To Transform Your Life Before 8AM*. In this book, which has since become an international bestseller, I introduced the world to the Life S.A.V.E.R.S. These success strategies have changed the lives of millions of people all around the world. After the success of *The Miracle Morning*, I partnered with Honorée Corder to produce The Miracle Morning Book Series, which extended *The Miracle Morning* to create titles such as *The Miracle Morning for Real Estate Agents*, *The Miracle Morning for Network Marketers*, *The Miracle Morning for Salespeople*, *The Miracle Morning for Parents and Families*, *The Miracle Morning Art of Affirmations*, *The Miracle Morning for Writers*, *The Miracle Morning for Entrepreneurs*, and *The Miracle Morning for Transforming Your Relationship*, among others.

In May 2017, Honorée and I created **The Miracle Morning for College Students** with college super star Natalie Janji. Now, we present **The Miracle Morning Companion Planner**. This planner will be the tool you need to implement the Life S.A.V.E.R.S. in your life and create the foundational schedule that will strengthen your self-leadership skills to build a better you. It will guide you to identify your priorities, break up larger tasks into many smaller tasks, organize your life, manage your time, and time-block to accomplish your goals. This planner furthers some of the most significant benefits of *The Miracle Morning*: to increase self-awareness, self-leadership, and to help you create productive habits in skills such as your work, social life, health, and any other ambitions you may have!

Before we go into how to use this planner, let's review the life-changing concept of the Life S.A.V.E.R.S. and how you can implement them in your life.

The Life S.A.V.E.R.S. is a compilation of six habits that have been practiced over centuries by the most successful and productive people in history.

"S" IS FOR SILENCE

Starting each day with a period of silence instead of looking at your phone or starting your busy day will immediately reduce your stress levels and help you begin the day with the calm and clarity that you need to focus on what's most important. You have a number of choices for your practice of silence. In no particular order, here are a few to get you started:

- Meditation

- Prayer

- Reflection

- Deep breathing

- Gratitude

Silence in the form of meditation reduces stress and, as a result, improves your health. A major study run by several groups, including the National Institutes of Health, the American Medical Association, the Mayo Clinic, and scientists from both Harvard and Stanford, revealed that meditation reduces stress and high blood pressure. A recent study by Dr. Norman Rosenthal, a world-renowned psychiatrist who works with the David Lynch Foundation, even found that people who practice meditation are 30 percent less likely to die from heart disease.

Meditation helps you to slow down and focus on you, even if it's for just a short time. Start your meditation practice and say goodbye to feeling scattered and wandering aimlessly without intention and purpose through your day.

Meditation is like anything else: if you've never done it before, it can be difficult or feel awkward at first. If you are a first-time meditator, I recommend starting with a guided meditation. A list of meditation apps is available in the Resources section in the back of the planner.

Think of daily meditation as a temporary vacation from the challenges of life. Although your problems will still be there when you finish each day, you'll find that you're more centered and better equipped to solve them.

"A" IS FOR AFFIRMATIONS

Reciting affirmations is a practice to strengthen your mindset. Mindset is the accumulation of your beliefs, attitude, and emotional intelligence. In her bestselling book, *Mindset: The New Psychology of*

Success, Carol Dweck, Ph.D., explains it this way: "For twenty years, my research has shown that the view you adopt of yourself profoundly affects the way you lead your life."

Science has proven that affirmations are one of the most effective tools for quickly becoming the person you need to be to achieve everything you want in your life—for yourself, your work, and your relationships.

Reciting affirmations is a tool to enable you to become more intentional about your goals while also providing the encouragement and positive mindset necessary to achieve them.

By repeatedly articulating and reinforcing to yourself *what* result you want to accomplish, *why* accomplishing it is important to you, *which* specific actions are required to produce that result, and, most importantly, precisely *when* you commit to taking those actions, your subconscious mind will shift your beliefs and behavior. You'll begin to believe your affirmations and behave in new ways, and eventually manifest your affirmations into your reality.

"V" IS FOR VISUALIZATION

Visualization has long been a well-known practice of world-class athletes, who use it to optimize their performance. Olympic athletes and top performers in many sports incorporate visualization as a critical part of their daily training. What is less well known is that the top achievers among successful entrepreneurs use it just as frequently.

Visualization is a technique by which you use your imagination to create a compelling picture of your future, providing you with heightened clarity and producing the motivation that will assist you in making your vision a reality.

Most people are limited by visions of their past results. They replay previous failures and heartbreaks. Creative visualization, however, enables you to *design* the vision that will occupy your mind, ensuring that the greatest pull on you is your future—a compelling, exciting, and limitless future. The perfect time to visualize yourself living in alignment with your affirmations is right after you read them.

Many people don't feel comfortable visualizing success and are even scared to succeed. They may experience resistance to this practice. Some may even feel guilty that they will leave colleagues, friends, and family members behind when they become successful. The greatest gift you can give to those you love and those you lead is to live to your full potential. What does that look like for you?

There is scientific evidence showing that merely visualizing the result you want (e.g., the new car, the dream house, crossing the finish line, standing on stage, etc.) can actually diminish your drive because your brain has already experienced the reward on some level. Instead, focus your visualization on the necessary actions. Visualize yourself performing the actions—especially those that you habitually resist and procrastinate on—in a way that creates a compelling mental and emotional experience of the action.

You might picture yourself enjoying getting your work done. Spend time imagining yourself effortlessly working on or completing a project, for example. What does it look like? How does it feel as you remain focused and make progress? Picture yourself responding to obstacles and issues with ease.

If any aspect of your life or business is a challenge for you, visualize yourself calmly, easily and successfully achieving your desired outcome. Imagine that you are excited to complete your tasks for the end results waiting for you when they are finished!

You can pick anything that is a critical action step or skill that you may not be performing at your best yet. Envisioning success and what it takes to get there will prepare you for, and almost ensure, a successful day.

"E" IS FOR EXERCISE

Exercise should be a staple of your Miracle Morning. Even a few minutes of exercise each day significantly enhances your health, improves your self-confidence and emotional well-being, and enables you to think better and concentrate longer. You'll also notice how quickly your energy increases with daily exercise, and the people you spend the most time with will notice it too.

You can go for a walk or run, follow along to a yoga video on YouTube, or find a Life S.A.V.E.R.S. buddy and play some early morning racquetball. There's also an excellent app called 7 Minute Workout that gives you a full body workout in—you guessed it—seven minutes. The choice is yours, but pick one activity and do it.

As a busy and productive person, you are most likely constantly on the go. You need an endless reserve of energy to make the best of the challenges that come your way, and a daily morning exercise practice is going to provide it.

If you want to maintain good health and increase your energy, you must exercise consistently. That's not news to anyone, and it is easy to make excuses. Two of the biggest are "I don't have time" and "I'm too tired." And those are just the first two on the list. There is no limit to the excuses you can think of. And the more creative you are, the more excuses you can find!

That's the beauty of incorporating exercise into your Miracle Morning—it happens before your day wears you out and before you've had hours to come up with new excuses. Because it comes first, the Miracle Morning is a surefire way to avoid those stumbling blocks and make exercise a daily habit.

Legal disclaimer: You should consult your physician before beginning any exercise regimen, especially if you are experiencing any physical pain, discomfort, disabilities, etc. You may need to modify or even refrain from an exercise routine to meet your individual needs.

"R" IS FOR READING

One of the fastest ways to achieve everything you want is to find successful people to be your role models. For every goal you have, there's a good chance an expert out there has already achieved the same thing or something similar. As Tony Robbins says, "Success leaves clues."

Fortunately, some of the best of the best have shared their stories in writing. And that means all those success blueprints are just waiting for anyone willing to invest the time in reading. Books are a limitless supply of help and mentorship right at your fingertips.

In addition to finding professional and personal confidence, you can transform your relationships, increase your self-esteem, improve your communication skills, learn how to become healthy, and improve any other area of your life you can think of. Head to your library or local bookstore—or do what we do and visit Amazon.com—and you'll find more books than you can possibly imagine on any area of your life you want to improve.

Make a commitment to read a minimum of ten pages per day (although five is okay to start with if you read slowly or don't yet enjoy reading). Ten pages may not seem like a lot, but let's do the math. Reading ten pages a day adds up to 3,650 pages per year, which stacks up to approximately eighteen 200-page books that will enable you to take yourself to the next level so that you can take your success in your academic and professional life to the next level. All in just 10–15 minutes of daily reading, or 15–30 minutes if you read more slowly.

"S" IS FOR SCRIBING

Scribing is simply another word for writing. The scribing element of your Miracle Morning enables you to write down what you're grateful for, as well as document your insights, ideas, breakthroughs, realizations, successes, and lessons learned, including any areas of opportunity, personal growth, or improvement.

Most Miracle Morning practitioners scribe in a journal for five to ten minutes during their Miracle Morning. By getting your thoughts out of your head and putting them in writing, you'll immediately gain heightened awareness, clarity, and valuable insights that you'd otherwise forget or be oblivious to.

Writing will give you the daily benefit of consciously directing your thoughts, but what's even more powerful are the insights you'll gain from reviewing your journals, from cover to cover, afterwards—especially at the end of the year. Another quote from Tony Robbins fits perfectly here (and we think you'll agree), "A life worth living is a life worth recording." Your life is absolutely worth recording.

Here are three simple steps to get started with journaling or improve your current journaling process.

1. **Choose a format: physical or digital.** You'll want to decide up front if you prefer a traditional, physical journal or a digital journal (on your computer or an app for your mobile device). If you aren't sure, experiment with both and see which feels best.

2. **Obtain the journal of your choice.** Almost anything can work, but when it comes to a physical journal, there is something to be said for a durable one that you enjoy looking at—after all, ideally you're going to have it for the rest of your life. I like to buy high quality leather journals with lines on the pages, but it's your journal, so choose what works best for you. Some people prefer journals without lines so they can draw or create mind maps. Others like to have a predated book with a page for each day of the year to help them stay accountable. Hal uses the 5-Minute Journal app, Honorée uses the Bullet Journal, and Natalie uses *The Miracle Morning for College Students Companion Planner*.

3. **Scribe daily.** You'll find endless things you can write about—notes from the book you're reading, a list of things you're grateful for, and your top three to five priorities for the day are good items to start with. Write whatever makes you feel good and helps you optimize your day. Don't worry about grammar, spelling, or punctuation. Your journal is a place to let your imagination run wild, so keep a muzzle on your inner critic and don't edit—just scribe!

For more information about each of the practices in the Life S.A.V.E.R.S., such as recommended books to read, sample affirmations, or sample journal questions, visit the References section in the back of this planner.

———————

You may have heard the phrase "Knowledge is power," but that is not necessarily accurate. *Implementation* of knowledge that is power. The Life S.A.V.E.R.S. has changed all of our lives. It was not because Hal wrote or Honorée and Natalie have read *The Miracle Morning* book many times, but because we have implemented these habits into our daily routines. This is why we created this planner for you. This planner will allow you to reinforce the knowledge you learned in *The Miracle Morning*. You will be able to accomplish your dreams and goals by practicing the Life S.A.V.E.R.S., having a written plan with dates and deadlines, and becoming aware of the steps you can take to improve every area of your life.

THE MIRACLE MORNING COMPANION PLANNER

This companion guide to *The Miracle Morning* will allow you to strengthen the positive habits you are developing that will increase your productivity, help you to organize your life and accelerate your success. Here is an overview of pages included in this planner:

- *Dreams-* Identify and write out your dreams

- *Vision Board-* Paste or draw pictures to create a visual representation of your dreams and goals that will travel with you everywhere you take this planner

- *Monthly Overview-* Write out your monthly goal(s), important events, projects with their deadlines for the entire month. You will also be able to write a reminder of the important dates that need to be transferred to your phone calendar, and also brainstorm any ideas that you have during the month

- *Monthly Reflection-* Answer questions to reflect upon your last month and focus on how to achieve in the next month

- *Weekly Overview-* Write out your weekly goal, action you took for each habit in the Life S.A.V.E.R.S., intention for the day, and daily gratitude. You will also be able to set your foundational schedule from 6:00am-11:30pm. Lastly, you'll be able to check off the items you need to have ready for the next day of Life S.A.V.E.R.S., classes, and other responsibilities

- *References*- This section has many resources including:

  - Meditation Apps

  - Sample Affirmations

  - List of Recommended Books

  - Sample Journal Questions

In the following pages, you will see a few samples about how you might use this planner.

Remember, this planner is *yours*. With this planner, you can design the Level 10 life you want to live. You are more than capable, worthy, and deserving of living your Level 10 vision. Practice and track the Life S.A.V.E.R.S. Each day, and watch your life transform right in front of your eyes.

Happy Planning!

MONTH OF: January	SUNDAY	MONDAY	TUESDAY
This Month's Goal Finish all projects & write book outline		1	2
	7	8	9
Important Events or Reminders to Transfer to My Phone 1. Dentist appointment 2. Babysitting Thursdays 3. 4. 5. 6. 7. 8. 9. 10.	14	15 Dentist 8 AM	16
	21	22	Outline Due 23
	28	Meeting 10 AM 29	Graphics Finalized 30

PROJECT NAME	TEAM PLAYERS	IMPORTANT DATES	DEADLINES
1. Marketing Presentation	Outline – Rogers Graphics – Jones	January 29th Meeting	Outline January 23rd
2. Social Media Strategy 02/2018	Facebook – Brown Twitter – Rogers LinkedIn – Martin	January 17th Meeting	Graphics Due January 30th
3.			
4.			

WEDNESDAY	THURSDAY	FRIDAY	SATURDAY
3	4	5	6 Movies with friends
10	11 Babysitting Riley's 6 pm	12	13
17 Team Meeting 9 AM	18 Babysitting Riley's 6 pm	19	20
24	25 Babysitting Riley's 6 pm	26	John's Bday 27
31 Register for new email system			

BRAINSTORM

Prosperity
Giving back and helping others- pick up leaves & volunteering

Planning ———————— Work

|
|
↓
SUCCESS

- Save up for new car
- 2018 goals?!
- Tutoring with April
- Team letters & inspiration

Week of:		Sunday		Monday		Tuesday	
This Week's Goal	S	10-min meditation ✓	S	10-min meditation ✓	S	10-min meditation ✓
	A	Recited them ✓	A	Wrote them ✓	A	Recited them ✓
Complete SAVERS & projects due next week	V	Pictured studying ✓	V	Pictured speaking ✓	V	Pictured studying ✓
	E	Pushups/Jumping jacks ✓	E	30 min jogging ✓	E	30 min Gym ✓
	R	15 pages TMM4CS ✓	R	20 pages TMM ✓	R	15 pages TMM ✓
	S	Journaling ✓	S	Reflect on reading ✓	S	Journaling ✓
Intention for the Day		◆ Prosperity		◆ Lead by example		◆ Happiness
Grateful for ...		◆ Friends		◆ My health		◆ Laughter

No matter what people tell you, words and ideas can change the world.

—ROBIN WILLIAMS

TO-DO LIST

Highest Priority

Finish Book Deadline

Definite Priority

Reading for Book Club

Lowest Priority

Clean bathroom

Habit to Work on This Week

Daily healthy breakfast

Time	Sunday	Time	Monday	Time	Tuesday
5:00		5:00		5:00	
5:30		5:30		5:30	
6:00		6:00		6:00	
6:30		6:30		6:30	
7:00		7:00		7:00	
7:30		7:30		7:30	
8:00		8:00	Meeting	8:00	
8:30		8:30		8:30	
9:00		9:00		9:00	Tutoring
9:30		9:30		9:30	
10:00		10:00		10:00	
10:30		10:30		10:30	
11:00		11:00		11:00	
11:30		11:30	Finish Assignments	11:30	
12:00		12:00		12:00	
12:30		12:30		12:30	
1:00		1:00	Meeting	1:00	Meeting
1:30		1:30		1:30	
2:00	Study	2:00		2:00	
2:30		2:30		2:30	
3:00	Finish Projects	3:00		3:00	
3:30		3:30		3:30	
4:00		4:00		4:00	
4:30		4:30		4:30	
5:00		5:00		5:00	
5:30	Work	5:30		5:30	
6:00		6:00		6:00	Work
6:30		6:30		6:30	
7:00		7:00		7:00	
7:30		7:30		7:30	
8:00		8:00		8:00	
8:30		8:30	Study	8:30	
9:00		9:00		9:00	
9:30		9:30		9:30	
10:00		10:00	Bed	10:00	
10:30	Bed	10:30		10:30	Bed
11:00		11:00		11:00	

Ready for tomorrow?		(✓)		(✓)		(✓)
ALARM		6:30 am ✓		6:00 am ✓		6:00 am ✓
CLOTHES		✓		Dress up ✓		
GLASS OF WATER		✓		✓		✓
SAVERS PREP		✓				
BEDTIME AFFIRMATIONS		Wrote them ✓		Recited them ✓		Wrote them ✓

Wednesday	Thursday	Friday	Saturday
S 10-min meditation ✓	S 10-min meditation ✓	S 10-min meditation ✓	S 10-min meditation ✓
A Recited them ✓	A Wrote them ✓	A Recited them ✓	A Wrote them ✓
V Pictured test-taking ✓	V Pictured studying ✓	V Pictured test-taking ✓	V Pictured studying ✓
E Pushups/Jumping jacks ✓	E 30 min jogging ✓	E Pushups/Jumping jacks ✓	E 30 min jogging ✓
R 15 pages TMMCS ✓	R 18 pages TMMCS ✓	R 15 pages TMMCS ✓	R 18 pages TMMCS ✓
S Reflect on reading ✓	S Journaling	S Reflect on reading ✓	S Journaling

◆ Help a stranger	◆ Forgiveness	◆ Lead by example	◆ Prosperity
◆ My mom	◆ Family time	◆ Laughter	◆ My health

Time	Wednesday	Thursday	Friday	Saturday
5:00				
5:30				
6:00				
6:30				
7:00				
7:30				
8:00	Meeting		Meeting	
8:30				
9:00		Tutoring		
9:30				
10:00				Study
10:30				
11:00				
11:30			Study	
12:00	Finish Assignments			
12:30				
1:00	Meeting	Meeting	Meeting	
1:30				
2:00				Finish Projects
2:30				
3:00				
3:30				
4:00				
4:30				
5:00				
5:30		Work	Work	
6:00				
6:30				Go out with friends
7:00				
7:30	Study			
8:00				
8:30				
9:00				
9:30				
10:00	Bed			
10:30		Bed		
11:00			Bed	Bed

(✓)	(✓)	(✓)	(✓)
6:00 am ✓	6:00 am ✓	6:00 am ✓	6:30 am ✓
Extra notepad ✓	Dress up ✓	Dress up ✓	Study notes ✓
✓	✓	✓	✓
Recited them ✓	Wrote them ✓	Recited them ✓	Recited them ✓

Love the life you have while you create the life of your dreams. Don't think you have to choose one over the other.

—HAL ELROD

DREAMS

· ·

Write out your dreams below ...

VISION BOARD

• •

Paste or draw pictures of your visions ...

MONTH OF:	SUNDAY	MONDAY	TUESDAY
This Month's Goal			
Important Events or Reminders to Transfer to My Phone			
1.			
2.			
3.			
4.			
5.			
6.			
7.			
8.			
9.			
10.			

PROJECT NAME	TEAM PLAYERS	IMPORTANT DATES	DEADLINES
1.			
2.			
3.			
4.			

WEDNESDAY	THURSDAY	FRIDAY	SATURDAY

BRAINSTORM

Week of:	Sunday	Monday	Tuesday
This Week's Goal	S	S	S
	A	A	A
	V	V	V
	E	E	E
	R	R	R
	S	S	S
Intention for the Day	◆	◆	◆
Grateful for …	◆	◆	◆

No matter what people tell you, words and ideas can change the world.

–ROBIN WILLIAMS

TO-DO LIST	Sunday	Monday	Tuesday
Highest Priority	5:00	5:00	5:00
	5:30	5:30	5:30
	6:00	6:00	6:00
	6:30	6:30	6:30
	7:00	7:00	7:00
	7:30	7:30	7:30
	8:00	8:00	8:00
	8:30	8:30	8:30
	9:00	9:00	9:00
	9:30	9:30	9:30
	10:00	10:00	10:00
	10:30	10:30	10:30
	11:00	11:00	11:00
	11:30	11:30	11:30
	12:00	12:00	12:00
	12:30	12:30	12:30
	1:00	1:00	1:00
Definite Priority	1:30	1:30	1:30
	2:00	2:00	2:00
	2:30	2:30	2:30
	3:00	3:00	3:00
	3:30	3:30	3:30
	4:00	4:00	4:00
Lowest Priority	4:30	4:30	4:30
	5:00	5:00	5:00
	5:30	5:30	5:30
	6:00	6:00	6:00
	6:30	6:30	6:30
	7:00	7:00	7:00
	7:30	7:30	7:30
Habit to Work on This Week	8:00	8:00	8:00
	8:30	8:30	8:30
	9:00	9:00	9:00
	9:30	9:30	9:30
	10:00	10:00	10:00
	10:30	10:30	10:30
	11:00	11:00	11:00

Ready for tomorrow?	( )	( )	( )
ALARM			
CLOTHES			
GLASS OF WATER			
SAVERS PREP			
BEDTIME AFFIRMATIONS			

Wednesday		Thursday		Friday		Saturday	
S		S		S		S	
A		A		A		A	
V		V		V		V	
E		E		E		E	
R		R		R		R	
S		S		S		S	
◆		◆		◆		◆	
◆		◆		◆		◆	
5:00		5:00		5:00		5:00	
5:30		5:30		5:30		5:30	
6:00		6:00		6:00		6:00	
6:30		6:30		6:30		6:30	
7:00		7:00		7:00		7:00	
7:30		7:30		7:30		7:30	
8:00		8:00		8:00		8:00	
8:30		8:30		8:30		8:30	
9:00		9:00		9:00		9:00	
9:30		9:30		9:30		9:30	
10:00		10:00		10:00		10:00	
10:30		10:30		10:30		10:30	
11:00		11:00		11:00		11:00	
11:30		11:30		11:30		11:30	
12:00		12:00		12:00		12:00	
12:30		12:30		12:30		12:30	
1:00		1:00		1:00		1:00	
1:30		1:30		1:30		1:30	
2:00		2:00		2:00		2:00	
2:30		2:30		2:30		2:30	
3:00		3:00		3:00		3:00	
3:30		3:30		3:30		3:30	
4:00		4:00		4:00		4:00	
4:30		4:30		4:30		4:30	
5:00		5:00		5:00		5:00	
5:30		5:30		5:30		5:30	
6:00		6:00		6:00		6:00	
6:30		6:30		6:30		6:30	
7:00		7:00		7:00		7:00	
7:30		7:30		7:30		7:30	
8:00		8:00		8:00		8:00	
8:30		8:30		8:30		8:30	
9:00		9:00		9:00		9:00	
9:30		9:30		9:30		9:30	
10:00		10:00		10:00		10:00	
10:30		10:30		10:30		10:30	
11:00		11:00		11:00		11:00	
	( )		( )		( )		( )

Week of:	Sunday	Monday	Tuesday
This Week's Goal	S	S	S
	A	A	A
	V	V	V
	E	E	E
	R	R	R
	S	S	S
Intention for the Day	◆	◆	◆
Grateful for ...	◆	◆	◆

We make a living by what we get. We make a life by what we give.

—WINSTON CHURCHILL

TO-DO LIST			
Highest Priority			

Definite Priority

Lowest Priority

Habit to Work on This Week

Time	Sunday	Monday	Tuesday
5:00			
5:30			
6:00			
6:30			
7:00			
7:30			
8:00			
8:30			
9:00			
9:30			
10:00			
10:30			
11:00			
11:30			
12:00			
12:30			
1:00			
1:30			
2:00			
2:30			
3:00			
3:30			
4:00			
4:30			
5:00			
5:30			
6:00			
6:30			
7:00			
7:30			
8:00			
8:30			
9:00			
9:30			
10:00			
10:30			
11:00			

Ready for tomorrow?	( )	( )	( )
ALARM			
CLOTHES			
GLASS OF WATER			
SAVERS PREP			
BEDTIME AFFIRMATIONS			

Wednesday	Thursday	Friday	Saturday
S	S	S	S
A	A	A	A
V	V	V	V
E	E	E	E
R	R	R	R
S	S	S	S

◆	◆	◆	◆
◆	◆	◆	◆

Wednesday	Thursday	Friday	Saturday
5:00	5:00	5:00	5:00
5:30	5:30	5:30	5:30
6:00	6:00	6:00	6:00
6:30	6:30	6:30	6:30
7:00	7:00	7:00	7:00
7:30	7:30	7:30	7:30
8:00	8:00	8:00	8:00
8:30	8:30	8:30	8:30
9:00	9:00	9:00	9:00
9:30	9:30	9:30	9:30
10:00	10:00	10:00	10:00
10:30	10:30	10:30	10:30
11:00	11:00	11:00	11:00
11:30	11:30	11:30	11:30
12:00	12:00	12:00	12:00
12:30	12:30	12:30	12:30
1:00	1:00	1:00	1:00
1:30	1:30	1:30	1:30
2:00	2:00	2:00	2:00
2:30	2:30	2:30	2:30
3:00	3:00	3:00	3:00
3:30	3:30	3:30	3:30
4:00	4:00	4:00	4:00
4:30	4:30	4:30	4:30
5:00	5:00	5:00	5:00
5:30	5:30	5:30	5:30
6:00	6:00	6:00	6:00
6:30	6:30	6:30	6:30
7:00	7:00	7:00	7:00
7:30	7:30	7:30	7:30
8:00	8:00	8:00	8:00
8:30	8:30	8:30	8:30
9:00	9:00	9:00	9:00
9:30	9:30	9:30	9:30
10:00	10:00	10:00	10:00
10:30	10:30	10:30	10:30
11:00	11:00	11:00	11:00

( )	( )	( )	( )

Week of:	Sunday	Monday	Tuesday
This Week's Goal	S	S	S
	A	A	A
	V	V	V
	E	E	E
	R	R	R
	S	S	S
Intention for the Day	◆	◆	◆
Grateful for …	◆	◆	◆

You've got to get up every morning with determination if you're going to go to bed with satisfaction.

—GEORGE LORIMER

TO-DO LIST			
Highest Priority			

	Sunday	Monday	Tuesday
5:00		5:00	5:00
5:30		5:30	5:30
6:00		6:00	6:00
6:30		6:30	6:30
7:00		7:00	7:00
7:30		7:30	7:30
8:00		8:00	8:00
8:30		8:30	8:30
9:00		9:00	9:00
9:30		9:30	9:30
10:00		10:00	10:00
10:30		10:30	10:30
11:00		11:00	11:00
11:30		11:30	11:30
12:00		12:00	12:00
12:30		12:30	12:30
1:00		1:00	1:00
1:30		1:30	1:30
2:00		2:00	2:00
2:30		2:30	2:30
3:00		3:00	3:00
3:30		3:30	3:30
4:00		4:00	4:00
4:30		4:30	4:30
5:00		5:00	5:00
5:30		5:30	5:30
6:00		6:00	6:00
6:30		6:30	6:30
7:00		7:00	7:00
7:30		7:30	7:30
8:00		8:00	8:00
8:30		8:30	8:30
9:00		9:00	9:00
9:30		9:30	9:30
10:00		10:00	10:00
10:30		10:30	10:30
11:00		11:00	11:00

Definite Priority

Lowest Priority

Habit to Work on This Week

Ready for tomorrow?	( )	( )	( )
ALARM			
CLOTHES			
GLASS OF WATER			
SAVERS PREP			
BEDTIME AFFIRMATIONS			

Wednesday	Thursday	Friday	Saturday
S	S	S	S
A	A	A	A
V	V	V	V
E	E	E	E
R	R	R	R
S	S	S	S

◆	◆	◆	◆
◆	◆	◆	◆

Wednesday		Thursday		Friday		Saturday	
5:00		5:00		5:00		5:00	
5:30		5:30		5:30		5:30	
6:00		6:00		6:00		6:00	
6:30		6:30		6:30		6:30	
7:00		7:00		7:00		7:00	
7:30		7:30		7:30		7:30	
8:00		8:00		8:00		8:00	
8:30		8:30		8:30		8:30	
9:00		9:00		9:00		9:00	
9:30		9:30		9:30		9:30	
10:00		10:00		10:00		10:00	
10:30		10:30		10:30		10:30	
11:00		11:00		11:00		11:00	
11:30		11:30		11:30		11:30	
12:00		12:00		12:00		12:00	
12:30		12:30		12:30		12:30	
1:00		1:00		1:00		1:00	
1:30		1:30		1:30		1:30	
2:00		2:00		2:00		2:00	
2:30		2:30		2:30		2:30	
3:00		3:00		3:00		3:00	
3:30		3:30		3:30		3:30	
4:00		4:00		4:00		4:00	
4:30		4:30		4:30		4:30	
5:00		5:00		5:00		5:00	
5:30		5:30		5:30		5:30	
6:00		6:00		6:00		6:00	
6:30		6:30		6:30		6:30	
7:00		7:00		7:00		7:00	
7:30		7:30		7:30		7:30	
8:00		8:00		8:00		8:00	
8:30		8:30		8:30		8:30	
9:00		9:00		9:00		9:00	
9:30		9:30		9:30		9:30	
10:00		10:00		10:00		10:00	
10:30		10:30		10:30		10:30	
11:00		11:00		11:00		11:00	

( )	( )	( )	( )

Week of:	Sunday	Monday	Tuesday
This Week's Goal	S	S	S
	A	A	A
	V	V	V
	E	E	E
	R	R	R
	S	S	S
Intention for the Day	◆	◆	◆
Grateful for ...	◆	◆	◆

Your level of success will seldom exceed your level of personal development ... because success is something you attract by the person you become.

—JIM ROHN

TO-DO LIST			
Highest Priority			

	Sunday	Monday	Tuesday
5:00		5:00	5:00
5:30		5:30	5:30
6:00		6:00	6:00
6:30		6:30	6:30
7:00		7:00	7:00
7:30		7:30	7:30
8:00		8:00	8:00
8:30		8:30	8:30
9:00		9:00	9:00
9:30		9:30	9:30
10:00		10:00	10:00
10:30		10:30	10:30
11:00		11:00	11:00
11:30		11:30	11:30
12:00		12:00	12:00
12:30		12:30	12:30
1:00		1:00	1:00
1:30		1:30	1:30
2:00		2:00	2:00
2:30		2:30	2:30
3:00		3:00	3:00
3:30		3:30	3:30
4:00		4:00	4:00
4:30		4:30	4:30
5:00		5:00	5:00
5:30		5:30	5:30
6:00		6:00	6:00
6:30		6:30	6:30
7:00		7:00	7:00
7:30		7:30	7:30
8:00		8:00	8:00
8:30		8:30	8:30
9:00		9:00	9:00
9:30		9:30	9:30
10:00		10:00	10:00
10:30		10:30	10:30
11:00		11:00	11:00

TO-DO LIST sub-sections (left column):
- **Highest Priority**
- **Definite Priority**
- **Lowest Priority**
- **Habit to Work on This Week**

Ready for tomorrow?	( )	( )	( )
ALARM			
CLOTHES			
GLASS OF WATER			
SAVERS PREP			
BEDTIME AFFIRMATIONS			

Wednesday		Thursday		Friday		Saturday	
S		S		S		S	
A		A		A		A	
V		V		V		V	
E		E		E		E	
R		R		R		R	
S		S		S		S	
◆		◆		◆		◆	
◆		◆		◆		◆	
5:00		5:00		5:00		5:00	
5:30		5:30		5:30		5:30	
6:00		6:00		6:00		6:00	
6:30		6:30		6:30		6:30	
7:00		7:00		7:00		7:00	
7:30		7:30		7:30		7:30	
8:00		8:00		8:00		8:00	
8:30		8:30		8:30		8:30	
9:00		9:00		9:00		9:00	
9:30		9:30		9:30		9:30	
10:00		10:00		10:00		10:00	
10:30		10:30		10:30		10:30	
11:00		11:00		11:00		11:00	
11:30		11:30		11:30		11:30	
12:00		12:00		12:00		12:00	
12:30		12:30		12:30		12:30	
1:00		1:00		1:00		1:00	
1:30		1:30		1:30		1:30	
2:00		2:00		2:00		2:00	
2:30		2:30		2:30		2:30	
3:00		3:00		3:00		3:00	
3:30		3:30		3:30		3:30	
4:00		4:00		4:00		4:00	
4:30		4:30		4:30		4:30	
5:00		5:00		5:00		5:00	
5:30		5:30		5:30		5:30	
6:00		6:00		6:00		6:00	
6:30		6:30		6:30		6:30	
7:00		7:00		7:00		7:00	
7:30		7:30		7:30		7:30	
8:00		8:00		8:00		8:00	
8:30		8:30		8:30		8:30	
9:00		9:00		9:00		9:00	
9:30		9:30		9:30		9:30	
10:00		10:00		10:00		10:00	
10:30		10:30		10:30		10:30	
11:00		11:00		11:00		11:00	
	( )		( )		( )		( )

Week of:	Sunday	Monday	Tuesday
This Week's Goal	S	S	S
	A	A	A
	V	V	V
	E	E	E
	R	R	R
	S	S	S
Intention for the Day	◆	◆	◆
Grateful for ...	◆	◆	◆

Make each day your masterpiece.

—JOHN WOODEN

TO-DO LIST
Highest Priority
Definite Priority
Lowest Priority
Habit to Work on This Week

Time	Sunday	Monday	Tuesday
5:00			
5:30			
6:00			
6:30			
7:00			
7:30			
8:00			
8:30			
9:00			
9:30			
10:00			
10:30			
11:00			
11:30			
12:00			
12:30			
1:00			
1:30			
2:00			
2:30			
3:00			
3:30			
4:00			
4:30			
5:00			
5:30			
6:00			
6:30			
7:00			
7:30			
8:00			
8:30			
9:00			
9:30			
10:00			
10:30			
11:00			

Ready for tomorrow?	( )	( )	( )
ALARM			
CLOTHES			
GLASS OF WATER			
SAVERS PREP			
BEDTIME AFFIRMATIONS			

Wednesday	Thursday	Friday	Saturday
S	S	S	S
A	A	A	A
V	V	V	V
E	E	E	E
R	R	R	R
S	S	S	S
◆	◆	◆	◆
◆	◆	◆	◆

Wednesday	Thursday	Friday	Saturday
5:00	5:00	5:00	5:00
5:30	5:30	5:30	5:30
6:00	6:00	6:00	6:00
6:30	6:30	6:30	6:30
7:00	7:00	7:00	7:00
7:30	7:30	7:30	7:30
8:00	8:00	8:00	8:00
8:30	8:30	8:30	8:30
9:00	9:00	9:00	9:00
9:30	9:30	9:30	9:30
10:00	10:00	10:00	10:00
10:30	10:30	10:30	10:30
11:00	11:00	11:00	11:00
11:30	11:30	11:30	11:30
12:00	12:00	12:00	12:00
12:30	12:30	12:30	12:30
1:00	1:00	1:00	1:00
1:30	1:30	1:30	1:30
2:00	2:00	2:00	2:00
2:30	2:30	2:30	2:30
3:00	3:00	3:00	3:00
3:30	3:30	3:30	3:30
4:00	4:00	4:00	4:00
4:30	4:30	4:30	4:30
5:00	5:00	5:00	5:00
5:30	5:30	5:30	5:30
6:00	6:00	6:00	6:00
6:30	6:30	6:30	6:30
7:00	7:00	7:00	7:00
7:30	7:30	7:30	7:30
8:00	8:00	8:00	8:00
8:30	8:30	8:30	8:30
9:00	9:00	9:00	9:00
9:30	9:30	9:30	9:30
10:00	10:00	10:00	10:00
10:30	10:30	10:30	10:30
11:00	11:00	11:00	11:00
( )	( )	( )	( )

MONTHLY REFLECTION

1.

2.

3.

4.

5.

QUESTIONS

1) What did I learn about myself this month?

2) What tasks are left over from this month that are lingering and need to get done?

3. Did I take care of myself?

4) What could I have done differently this past month?

5) What areas can I (still) improve on?

6) What experiences can I treasure?

7) What challenged me and how did I overcome the challenge?

8) What specific habits and/or rituals could I develop this month to support my vision?

MONTH OF:	SUNDAY	MONDAY	TUESDAY
This Month's Goal			
Important Events or Reminders to Transfer to My Phone			
1.			
2.			
3.			
4.			
5.			
6.			
7.			
8.			
9.			
10.			
PROJECT NAME	**TEAM PLAYERS**	**IMPORTANT DATES**	**DEADLINES**
1.			
2.			
3.			
4.			

WEDNESDAY	THURSDAY	FRIDAY	SATURDAY

BRAINSTORM

Week of:	Sunday	Monday	Tuesday
This Week's Goal	S	S	S
	A	A	A
	V	V	V
	E	E	E
	R	R	R
	S	S	S
Intention for the Day	◆	◆	◆
Grateful for ...	◆	◆	◆

Remember, the moment you accept total responsibility for everything in your life is the moment you claim the power to change anything in your life.

—HAL ELROD

TO-DO LIST
Highest Priority
Definite Priority
Lowest Priority
Habit to Work on This Week

	Sunday	Monday	Tuesday
5:00		5:00		5:00	
5:30		5:30		5:30	
6:00		6:00		6:00	
6:30		6:30		6:30	
7:00		7:00		7:00	
7:30		7:30		7:30	
8:00		8:00		8:00	
8:30		8:30		8:30	
9:00		9:00		9:00	
9:30		9:30		9:30	
10:00		10:00		10:00	
10:30		10:30		10:30	
11:00		11:00		11:00	
11:30		11:30		11:30	
12:00		12:00		12:00	
12:30		12:30		12:30	
1:00		1:00		1:00	
1:30		1:30		1:30	
2:00		2:00		2:00	
2:30		2:30		2:30	
3:00		3:00		3:00	
3:30		3:30		3:30	
4:00		4:00		4:00	
4:30		4:30		4:30	
5:00		5:00		5:00	
5:30		5:30		5:30	
6:00		6:00		6:00	
6:30		6:30		6:30	
7:00		7:00		7:00	
7:30		7:30		7:30	
8:00		8:00		8:00	
8:30		8:30		8:30	
9:00		9:00		9:00	
9:30		9:30		9:30	
10:00		10:00		10:00	
10:30		10:30		10:30	
11:00		11:00		11:00	

Ready for tomorrow?	( )	( )	( )
ALARM			
CLOTHES			
GLASS OF WATER			
SAVERS PREP			
BEDTIME AFFIRMATIONS			

Wednesday	Thursday	Friday	Saturday
S	S	S	S
A	A	A	A
V	V	V	V
E	E	E	E
R	R	R	R
S	S	S	S
◆	◆	◆	◆
◆	◆	◆	◆

5:00		5:00		5:00		5:00	
5:30		5:30		5:30		5:30	
6:00		6:00		6:00		6:00	
6:30		6:30		6:30		6:30	
7:00		7:00		7:00		7:00	
7:30		7:30		7:30		7:30	
8:00		8:00		8:00		8:00	
8:30		8:30		8:30		8:30	
9:00		9:00		9:00		9:00	
9:30		9:30		9:30		9:30	
10:00		10:00		10:00		10:00	
10:30		10:30		10:30		10:30	
11:00		11:00		11:00		11:00	
11:30		11:30		11:30		11:30	
12:00		12:00		12:00		12:00	
12:30		12:30		12:30		12:30	
1:00		1:00		1:00		1:00	
1:30		1:30		1:30		1:30	
2:00		2:00		2:00		2:00	
2:30		2:30		2:30		2:30	
3:00		3:00		3:00		3:00	
3:30		3:30		3:30		3:30	
4:00		4:00		4:00		4:00	
4:30		4:30		4:30		4:30	
5:00		5:00		5:00		5:00	
5:30		5:30		5:30		5:30	
6:00		6:00		6:00		6:00	
6:30		6:30		6:30		6:30	
7:00		7:00		7:00		7:00	
7:30		7:30		7:30		7:30	
8:00		8:00		8:00		8:00	
8:30		8:30		8:30		8:30	
9:00		9:00		9:00		9:00	
9:30		9:30		9:30		9:30	
10:00		10:00		10:00		10:00	
10:30		10:30		10:30		10:30	
11:00		11:00		11:00		11:00	

( )	( )	( )	( )

Week of:	Sunday	Monday	Tuesday
This Week's Goal	S	S	S
	A	A	A
	V	V	V
	E	E	E
	R	R	R
	S	S	S
Intention for the Day	◆	◆	◆
Grateful for ...	◆	◆	◆

To make profound changes in your life, you need either inspiration or desperation.

—ANTHONY ROBBINS

TO-DO LIST
Highest Priority
Definite Priority
Lowest Priority
Habit to Work on This Week

Time	Sunday	Monday	Tuesday
5:00			
5:30			
6:00			
6:30			
7:00			
7:30			
8:00			
8:30			
9:00			
9:30			
10:00			
10:30			
11:00			
11:30			
12:00			
12:30			
1:00			
1:30			
2:00			
2:30			
3:00			
3:30			
4:00			
4:30			
5:00			
5:30			
6:00			
6:30			
7:00			
7:30			
8:00			
8:30			
9:00			
9:30			
10:00			
10:30			
11:00			

Ready for tomorrow?	( )	( )	( )
ALARM			
CLOTHES			
GLASS OF WATER			
SAVERS PREP			
BEDTIME AFFIRMATIONS			

Wednesday	Thursday	Friday	Saturday
S	S	S	S
A	A	A	A
V	V	V	V
E	E	E	E
R	R	R	R
S	S	S	S

◆	◆	◆	◆
◆	◆	◆	◆

Wednesday	Thursday	Friday	Saturday
5:00	5:00	5:00	5:00
5:30	5:30	5:30	5:30
6:00	6:00	6:00	6:00
6:30	6:30	6:30	6:30
7:00	7:00	7:00	7:00
7:30	7:30	7:30	7:30
8:00	8:00	8:00	8:00
8:30	8:30	8:30	8:30
9:00	9:00	9:00	9:00
9:30	9:30	9:30	9:30
10:00	10:00	10:00	10:00
10:30	10:30	10:30	10:30
11:00	11:00	11:00	11:00
11:30	11:30	11:30	11:30
12:00	12:00	12:00	12:00
12:30	12:30	12:30	12:30
1:00	1:00	1:00	1:00
1:30	1:30	1:30	1:30
2:00	2:00	2:00	2:00
2:30	2:30	2:30	2:30
3:00	3:00	3:00	3:00
3:30	3:30	3:30	3:30
4:00	4:00	4:00	4:00
4:30	4:30	4:30	4:30
5:00	5:00	5:00	5:00
5:30	5:30	5:30	5:30
6:00	6:00	6:00	6:00
6:30	6:30	6:30	6:30
7:00	7:00	7:00	7:00
7:30	7:30	7:30	7:30
8:00	8:00	8:00	8:00
8:30	8:30	8:30	8:30
9:00	9:00	9:00	9:00
9:30	9:30	9:30	9:30
10:00	10:00	10:00	10:00
10:30	10:30	10:30	10:30
11:00	11:00	11:00	11:00

( )	( )	( )	( )

Week of:	Sunday	Monday	Tuesday
This Week's Goal	S	S	S
	A	A	A
	V	V	V
	E	E	E
	R	R	R
	S	S	S
Intention for the Day	◆	◆	◆
Grateful for ...	◆	◆	◆

Don't chase money. Chase excellence.

—JEFF HOFFMAN

TO-DO LIST	Sunday	Monday	Tuesday
Highest Priority	5:00	5:00	5:00
	5:30	5:30	5:30
	6:00	6:00	6:00
	6:30	6:30	6:30
	7:00	7:00	7:00
	7:30	7:30	7:30
	8:00	8:00	8:00
	8:30	8:30	8:30
	9:00	9:00	9:00
	9:30	9:30	9:30
	10:00	10:00	10:00
	10:30	10:30	10:30
	11:00	11:00	11:00
	11:30	11:30	11:30
	12:00	12:00	12:00
	12:30	12:30	12:30
	1:00	1:00	1:00
Definite Priority	1:30	1:30	1:30
	2:00	2:00	2:00
	2:30	2:30	2:30
	3:00	3:00	3:00
	3:30	3:30	3:30
	4:00	4:00	4:00
Lowest Priority	4:30	4:30	4:30
	5:00	5:00	5:00
	5:30	5:30	5:30
	6:00	6:00	6:00
	6:30	6:30	6:30
	7:00	7:00	7:00
	7:30	7:30	7:30
Habit to Work on This Week	8:00	8:00	8:00
	8:30	8:30	8:30
	9:00	9:00	9:00
	9:30	9:30	9:30
	10:00	10:00	10:00
	10:30	10:30	10:30
	11:00	11:00	11:00

Ready for tomorrow?	( )	( )	( )
ALARM			
CLOTHES			
GLASS OF WATER			
SAVERS PREP			
BEDTIME AFFIRMATIONS			

Wednesday	Thursday	Friday	Saturday
S	S	S	S
A	A	A	A
V	V	V	V
E	E	E	E
R	R	R	R
S	S	S	S
◆	◆	◆	◆
◆	◆	◆	◆

Wednesday		Thursday		Friday		Saturday	
5:00		5:00		5:00		5:00	
5:30		5:30		5:30		5:30	
6:00		6:00		6:00		6:00	
6:30		6:30		6:30		6:30	
7:00		7:00		7:00		7:00	
7:30		7:30		7:30		7:30	
8:00		8:00		8:00		8:00	
8:30		8:30		8:30		8:30	
9:00		9:00		9:00		9:00	
9:30		9:30		9:30		9:30	
10:00		10:00		10:00		10:00	
10:30		10:30		10:30		10:30	
11:00		11:00		11:00		11:00	
11:30		11:30		11:30		11:30	
12:00		12:00		12:00		12:00	
12:30		12:30		12:30		12:30	
1:00		1:00		1:00		1:00	
1:30		1:30		1:30		1:30	
2:00		2:00		2:00		2:00	
2:30		2:30		2:30		2:30	
3:00		3:00		3:00		3:00	
3:30		3:30		3:30		3:30	
4:00		4:00		4:00		4:00	
4:30		4:30		4:30		4:30	
5:00		5:00		5:00		5:00	
5:30		5:30		5:30		5:30	
6:00		6:00		6:00		6:00	
6:30		6:30		6:30		6:30	
7:00		7:00		7:00		7:00	
7:30		7:30		7:30		7:30	
8:00		8:00		8:00		8:00	
8:30		8:30		8:30		8:30	
9:00		9:00		9:00		9:00	
9:30		9:30		9:30		9:30	
10:00		10:00		10:00		10:00	
10:30		10:30		10:30		10:30	
11:00		11:00		11:00		11:00	
	( )		( )		( )		( )

Week of:	Sunday		Monday		Tuesday	
This Week's Goal	S		S		S	
	A		A		A	
	V		V		V	
	E		E		E	
	R		R		R	
	S		S		S	
Intention for the Day	◆		◆		◆	
Grateful for ...	◆		◆		◆	

If you look at what you have in life, you'll always have more. If you look at what you don't have in life, you'll never have enough.

—OPRAH WINFREY

	Sunday	Monday	Tuesday
TO-DO LIST			
Highest Priority	5:00	5:00	5:00
	5:30	5:30	5:30
	6:00	6:00	6:00
	6:30	6:30	6:30
	7:00	7:00	7:00
	7:30	7:30	7:30
	8:00	8:00	8:00
	8:30	8:30	8:30
	9:00	9:00	9:00
	9:30	9:30	9:30
	10:00	10:00	10:00
	10:30	10:30	10:30
	11:00	11:00	11:00
	11:30	11:30	11:30
	12:00	12:00	12:00
	12:30	12:30	12:30
	1:00	1:00	1:00
Definite Priority	1:30	1:30	1:30
	2:00	2:00	2:00
	2:30	2:30	2:30
	3:00	3:00	3:00
	3:30	3:30	3:30
	4:00	4:00	4:00
Lowest Priority	4:30	4:30	4:30
	5:00	5:00	5:00
	5:30	5:30	5:30
	6:00	6:00	6:00
	6:30	6:30	6:30
	7:00	7:00	7:00
	7:30	7:30	7:30
Habit to Work on This Week	8:00	8:00	8:00
	8:30	8:30	8:30
	9:00	9:00	9:00
	9:30	9:30	9:30
	10:00	10:00	10:00
	10:30	10:30	10:30
	11:00	11:00	11:00

Ready for tomorrow?	( )	( )	( )
ALARM			
CLOTHES			
GLASS OF WATER			
SAVERS PREP			
BEDTIME AFFIRMATIONS			

Wednesday		Thursday		Friday		Saturday	
S		S		S		S	
A		A		A		A	
V		V		V		V	
E		E		E		E	
R		R		R		R	
S		S		S		S	
◆		◆		◆		◆	
◆		◆		◆		◆	
5:00		5:00		5:00		5:00	
5:30		5:30		5:30		5:30	
6:00		6:00		6:00		6:00	
6:30		6:30		6:30		6:30	
7:00		7:00		7:00		7:00	
7:30		7:30		7:30		7:30	
8:00		8:00		8:00		8:00	
8:30		8:30		8:30		8:30	
9:00		9:00		9:00		9:00	
9:30		9:30		9:30		9:30	
10:00		10:00		10:00		10:00	
10:30		10:30		10:30		10:30	
11:00		11:00		11:00		11:00	
11:30		11:30		11:30		11:30	
12:00		12:00		12:00		12:00	
12:30		12:30		12:30		12:30	
1:00		1:00		1:00		1:00	
1:30		1:30		1:30		1:30	
2:00		2:00		2:00		2:00	
2:30		2:30		2:30		2:30	
3:00		3:00		3:00		3:00	
3:30		3:30		3:30		3:30	
4:00		4:00		4:00		4:00	
4:30		4:30		4:30		4:30	
5:00		5:00		5:00		5:00	
5:30		5:30		5:30		5:30	
6:00		6:00		6:00		6:00	
6:30		6:30		6:30		6:30	
7:00		7:00		7:00		7:00	
7:30		7:30		7:30		7:30	
8:00		8:00		8:00		8:00	
8:30		8:30		8:30		8:30	
9:00		9:00		9:00		9:00	
9:30		9:30		9:30		9:30	
10:00		10:00		10:00		10:00	
10:30		10:30		10:30		10:30	
11:00		11:00		11:00		11:00	
	( )		( )		( )		( )

Week of:	Sunday	Monday	Tuesday
This Week's Goal	S	S	S
	A	A	A
	V	V	V
	E	E	E
	R	R	R
	S	S	S
Intention for the Day	◆	◆	◆
Grateful for ...	◆	◆	◆

*Set an incredible goal-
not to achieve the goal
itself- but to become
who you must become
to achieve it.*

—HONORÉE CORDER

TO-DO LIST
Highest Priority
Definite Priority
Lowest Priority
Habit to Work on This Week

Time	Sunday	Monday	Tuesday
5:00			
5:30			
6:00			
6:30			
7:00			
7:30			
8:00			
8:30			
9:00			
9:30			
10:00			
10:30			
11:00			
11:30			
12:00			
12:30			
1:00			
1:30			
2:00			
2:30			
3:00			
3:30			
4:00			
4:30			
5:00			
5:30			
6:00			
6:30			
7:00			
7:30			
8:00			
8:30			
9:00			
9:30			
10:00			
10:30			
11:00			

Ready for tomorrow?	( )	( )	( )
ALARM			
CLOTHES			
GLASS OF WATER			
SAVERS PREP			
BEDTIME AFFIRMATIONS			

Wednesday	Thursday	Friday	Saturday
S	S	S	S
A	A	A	A
V	V	V	V
E	E	E	E
R	R	R	R
S	S	S	S

	◆		◆		◆		◆
	◆		◆		◆		◆

Wednesday	Thursday	Friday	Saturday
5:00	5:00	5:00	5:00
5:30	5:30	5:30	5:30
6:00	6:00	6:00	6:00
6:30	6:30	6:30	6:30
7:00	7:00	7:00	7:00
7:30	7:30	7:30	7:30
8:00	8:00	8:00	8:00
8:30	8:30	8:30	8:30
9:00	9:00	9:00	9:00
9:30	9:30	9:30	9:30
10:00	10:00	10:00	10:00
10:30	10:30	10:30	10:30
11:00	11:00	11:00	11:00
11:30	11:30	11:30	11:30
12:00	12:00	12:00	12:00
12:30	12:30	12:30	12:30
1:00	1:00	1:00	1:00
1:30	1:30	1:30	1:30
2:00	2:00	2:00	2:00
2:30	2:30	2:30	2:30
3:00	3:00	3:00	3:00
3:30	3:30	3:30	3:30
4:00	4:00	4:00	4:00
4:30	4:30	4:30	4:30
5:00	5:00	5:00	5:00
5:30	5:30	5:30	5:30
6:00	6:00	6:00	6:00
6:30	6:30	6:30	6:30
7:00	7:00	7:00	7:00
7:30	7:30	7:30	7:30
8:00	8:00	8:00	8:00
8:30	8:30	8:30	8:30
9:00	9:00	9:00	9:00
9:30	9:30	9:30	9:30
10:00	10:00	10:00	10:00
10:30	10:30	10:30	10:30
11:00	11:00	11:00	11:00

( )	( )	( )	( )

MONTHLY REFLECTION

· ·

Write 5 things you accomplished this month:

1.

2.

3.

4.

5.

QUESTIONS

1) What did I learn about myself this month?

2) What tasks are left over from this month that are lingering and need to get done?

3. Did I take care of myself?

4) What could I have done differently this past month?

5) What areas can I (still) improve on?

6) What experiences can I treasure?

7) What challenged me and how did I overcome the challenge?

8) What specific habits and/or rituals could I develop this month to support my vision?

MONTH OF:	SUNDAY	MONDAY	TUESDAY
This Month's Goal			
Important Events or Reminders to Transfer to My Phone			
1.			
2.			
3.			
4.			
5.			
6.			
7.			
8.			
9.			
10.			

PROJECT NAME	TEAM PLAYERS	IMPORTANT DATES	DEADLINES
1.			
2.			
3.			
4.			

WEDNESDAY	THURSDAY	FRIDAY	SATURDAY

BRAINSTORM

Week of:	Sunday	Monday	Tuesday
This Week's Goal	S	S	S
	A	A	A
	V	V	V
	E	E	E
	R	R	R
	S	S	S
Intention for the Day	◆	◆	◆
Grateful for ...	◆	◆	◆

Two roads diverged in a wood, and I—I took the one less traveled by, And that has made all the difference.

—ROBERT FROST

TO-DO LIST
Highest Priority
Definite Priority
Lowest Priority
Habit to Work on This Week

Time	Sunday	Monday	Tuesday
5:00			
5:30			
6:00			
6:30			
7:00			
7:30			
8:00			
8:30			
9:00			
9:30			
10:00			
10:30			
11:00			
11:30			
12:00			
12:30			
1:00			
1:30			
2:00			
2:30			
3:00			
3:30			
4:00			
4:30			
5:00			
5:30			
6:00			
6:30			
7:00			
7:30			
8:00			
8:30			
9:00			
9:30			
10:00			
10:30			
11:00			

Ready for tomorrow?	( )	( )	( )
ALARM			
CLOTHES			
GLASS OF WATER			
SAVERS PREP			
BEDTIME AFFIRMATIONS			

Wednesday		Thursday		Friday		Saturday	
S		S		S		S	
A		A		A		A	
V		V		V		V	
E		E		E		E	
R		R		R		R	
S		S		S		S	
◆		◆		◆		◆	
◆		◆		◆		◆	
5:00		5:00		5:00		5:00	
5:30		5:30		5:30		5:30	
6:00		6:00		6:00		6:00	
6:30		6:30		6:30		6:30	
7:00		7:00		7:00		7:00	
7:30		7:30		7:30		7:30	
8:00		8:00		8:00		8:00	
8:30		8:30		8:30		8:30	
9:00		9:00		9:00		9:00	
9:30		9:30		9:30		9:30	
10:00		10:00		10:00		10:00	
10:30		10:30		10:30		10:30	
11:00		11:00		11:00		11:00	
11:30		11:30		11:30		11:30	
12:00		12:00		12:00		12:00	
12:30		12:30		12:30		12:30	
1:00		1:00		1:00		1:00	
1:30		1:30		1:30		1:30	
2:00		2:00		2:00		2:00	
2:30		2:30		2:30		2:30	
3:00		3:00		3:00		3:00	
3:30		3:30		3:30		3:30	
4:00		4:00		4:00		4:00	
4:30		4:30		4:30		4:30	
5:00		5:00		5:00		5:00	
5:30		5:30		5:30		5:30	
6:00		6:00		6:00		6:00	
6:30		6:30		6:30		6:30	
7:00		7:00		7:00		7:00	
7:30		7:30		7:30		7:30	
8:00		8:00		8:00		8:00	
8:30		8:30		8:30		8:30	
9:00		9:00		9:00		9:00	
9:30		9:30		9:30		9:30	
10:00		10:00		10:00		10:00	
10:30		10:30		10:30		10:30	
11:00		11:00		11:00		11:00	
( )		( )		( )		( )	

Week of:	Sunday	Monday	Tuesday
This Week's Goal	S	S	S
	A	A	A
	V	V	V
	E	E	E
	R	R	R
	S	S	S
Intention for the Day	◆	◆	◆
Grateful for ...	◆	◆	◆

Give up being perfect for being authentic.

—HAL ELROD

	Sunday	Monday	Tuesday
	5:00	5:00	5:00
	5:30	5:30	5:30
	6:00	6:00	6:00
	6:30	6:30	6:30
	7:00	7:00	7:00
	7:30	7:30	7:30
	8:00	8:00	8:00
	8:30	8:30	8:30
	9:00	9:00	9:00
	9:30	9:30	9:30
TO-DO LIST	10:00	10:00	10:00
Highest Priority	10:30	10:30	10:30
	11:00	11:00	11:00
	11:30	11:30	11:30
	12:00	12:00	12:00
	12:30	12:30	12:30
	1:00	1:00	1:00
Definite Priority	1:30	1:30	1:30
	2:00	2:00	2:00
	2:30	2:30	2:30
	3:00	3:00	3:00
	3:30	3:30	3:30
	4:00	4:00	4:00
Lowest Priority	4:30	4:30	4:30
	5:00	5:00	5:00
	5:30	5:30	5:30
	6:00	6:00	6:00
	6:30	6:30	6:30
	7:00	7:00	7:00
	7:30	7:30	7:30
Habit to Work on This Week	8:00	8:00	8:00
	8:30	8:30	8:30
	9:00	9:00	9:00
	9:30	9:30	9:30
	10:00	10:00	10:00
	10:30	10:30	10:30
	11:00	11:00	11:00

Ready for tomorrow?	( )	( )	( )
ALARM			
CLOTHES			
GLASS OF WATER			
SAVERS PREP			
BEDTIME AFFIRMATIONS			

Wednesday		Thursday		Friday		Saturday	
S		S		S		S	
A		A		A		A	
V		V		V		V	
E		E		E		E	
R		R		R		R	
S		S		S		S	
◆		◆		◆		◆	
◆		◆		◆		◆	
5:00		5:00		5:00		5:00	
5:30		5:30		5:30		5:30	
6:00		6:00		6:00		6:00	
6:30		6:30		6:30		6:30	
7:00		7:00		7:00		7:00	
7:30		7:30		7:30		7:30	
8:00		8:00		8:00		8:00	
8:30		8:30		8:30		8:30	
9:00		9:00		9:00		9:00	
9:30		9:30		9:30		9:30	
10:00		10:00		10:00		10:00	
10:30		10:30		10:30		10:30	
11:00		11:00		11:00		11:00	
11:30		11:30		11:30		11:30	
12:00		12:00		12:00		12:00	
12:30		12:30		12:30		12:30	
1:00		1:00		1:00		1:00	
1:30		1:30		1:30		1:30	
2:00		2:00		2:00		2:00	
2:30		2:30		2:30		2:30	
3:00		3:00		3:00		3:00	
3:30		3:30		3:30		3:30	
4:00		4:00		4:00		4:00	
4:30		4:30		4:30		4:30	
5:00		5:00		5:00		5:00	
5:30		5:30		5:30		5:30	
6:00		6:00		6:00		6:00	
6:30		6:30		6:30		6:30	
7:00		7:00		7:00		7:00	
7:30		7:30		7:30		7:30	
8:00		8:00		8:00		8:00	
8:30		8:30		8:30		8:30	
9:00		9:00		9:00		9:00	
9:30		9:30		9:30		9:30	
10:00		10:00		10:00		10:00	
10:30		10:30		10:30		10:30	
11:00		11:00		11:00		11:00	
	( )		( )		( )		( )

Week of:	Sunday		Monday		Tuesday	
This Week's Goal	S		S		S	
	A		A		A	
	V		V		V	
	E		E		E	
	R		R		R	
	S		S		S	
Intention for the Day	◆		◆		◆	
Grateful for ...	◆		◆		◆	

	Sunday	Monday	Tuesday
When one door of happiness closes, another opens, but often we look so long at the closed door that we do not see the one that has been opened for us. —HELEN KELLER	5:00	5:00	5:00
	5:30	5:30	5:30
	6:00	6:00	6:00
	6:30	6:30	6:30
	7:00	7:00	7:00
	7:30	7:30	7:30
	8:00	8:00	8:00
	8:30	8:30	8:30
	9:00	9:00	9:00
	9:30	9:30	9:30
TO-DO LIST / Highest Priority	10:00	10:00	10:00
	10:30	10:30	10:30
	11:00	11:00	11:00
	11:30	11:30	11:30
	12:00	12:00	12:00
	12:30	12:30	12:30
	1:00	1:00	1:00
Definite Priority	1:30	1:30	1:30
	2:00	2:00	2:00
	2:30	2:30	2:30
	3:00	3:00	3:00
	3:30	3:30	3:30
	4:00	4:00	4:00
Lowest Priority	4:30	4:30	4:30
	5:00	5:00	5:00
	5:30	5:30	5:30
	6:00	6:00	6:00
	6:30	6:30	6:30
	7:00	7:00	7:00
	7:30	7:30	7:30
Habit to Work on This Week	8:00	8:00	8:00
	8:30	8:30	8:30
	9:00	9:00	9:00
	9:30	9:30	9:30
	10:00	10:00	10:00
	10:30	10:30	10:30
	11:00	11:00	11:00

Ready for tomorrow?	( )	( )	( )
ALARM			
CLOTHES			
GLASS OF WATER			
SAVERS PREP			
BEDTIME AFFIRMATIONS			

Wednesday		Thursday		Friday		Saturday	
S		S		S		S	
A		A		A		A	
V		V		V		V	
E		E		E		E	
R		R		R		R	
S		S		S		S	
◆		◆		◆		◆	
◆		◆		◆		◆	
5:00		5:00		5:00		5:00	
5:30		5:30		5:30		5:30	
6:00		6:00		6:00		6:00	
6:30		6:30		6:30		6:30	
7:00		7:00		7:00		7:00	
7:30		7:30		7:30		7:30	
8:00		8:00		8:00		8:00	
8:30		8:30		8:30		8:30	
9:00		9:00		9:00		9:00	
9:30		9:30		9:30		9:30	
10:00		10:00		10:00		10:00	
10:30		10:30		10:30		10:30	
11:00		11:00		11:00		11:00	
11:30		11:30		11:30		11:30	
12:00		12:00		12:00		12:00	
12:30		12:30		12:30		12:30	
1:00		1:00		1:00		1:00	
1:30		1:30		1:30		1:30	
2:00		2:00		2:00		2:00	
2:30		2:30		2:30		2:30	
3:00		3:00		3:00		3:00	
3:30		3:30		3:30		3:30	
4:00		4:00		4:00		4:00	
4:30		4:30		4:30		4:30	
5:00		5:00		5:00		5:00	
5:30		5:30		5:30		5:30	
6:00		6:00		6:00		6:00	
6:30		6:30		6:30		6:30	
7:00		7:00		7:00		7:00	
7:30		7:30		7:30		7:30	
8:00		8:00		8:00		8:00	
8:30		8:30		8:30		8:30	
9:00		9:00		9:00		9:00	
9:30		9:30		9:30		9:30	
10:00		10:00		10:00		10:00	
10:30		10:30		10:30		10:30	
11:00		11:00		11:00		11:00	
	( )		( )		( )		( )

Week of:	Sunday	Monday	Tuesday
This Week's Goal	S	S	S
	A	A	A
	V	V	V
	E	E	E
	R	R	R
	S	S	S
Intention for the Day	◆	◆	◆
Grateful for ...	◆	◆	◆

Success is something you attract by the person you become.

—JIM ROHN

TO-DO LIST

Highest Priority

Definite Priority

Lowest Priority

Habit to Work on This Week

Time	Sunday	Monday	Tuesday
5:00			
5:30			
6:00			
6:30			
7:00			
7:30			
8:00			
8:30			
9:00			
9:30			
10:00			
10:30			
11:00			
11:30			
12:00			
12:30			
1:00			
1:30			
2:00			
2:30			
3:00			
3:30			
4:00			
4:30			
5:00			
5:30			
6:00			
6:30			
7:00			
7:30			
8:00			
8:30			
9:00			
9:30			
10:00			
10:30			
11:00			

Ready for tomorrow?	( )	( )	( )
ALARM			
CLOTHES			
GLASS OF WATER			
SAVERS PREP			
BEDTIME AFFIRMATIONS			

Wednesday		Thursday		Friday		Saturday	
S		S		S		S	
A		A		A		A	
V		V		V		V	
E		E		E		E	
R		R		R		R	
S		S		S		S	
◆		◆		◆		◆	
◆		◆		◆		◆	
5:00		5:00		5:00		5:00	
5:30		5:30		5:30		5:30	
6:00		6:00		6:00		6:00	
6:30		6:30		6:30		6:30	
7:00		7:00		7:00		7:00	
7:30		7:30		7:30		7:30	
8:00		8:00		8:00		8:00	
8:30		8:30		8:30		8:30	
9:00		9:00		9:00		9:00	
9:30		9:30		9:30		9:30	
10:00		10:00		10:00		10:00	
10:30		10:30		10:30		10:30	
11:00		11:00		11:00		11:00	
11:30		11:30		11:30		11:30	
12:00		12:00		12:00		12:00	
12:30		12:30		12:30		12:30	
1:00		1:00		1:00		1:00	
1:30		1:30		1:30		1:30	
2:00		2:00		2:00		2:00	
2:30		2:30		2:30		2:30	
3:00		3:00		3:00		3:00	
3:30		3:30		3:30		3:30	
4:00		4:00		4:00		4:00	
4:30		4:30		4:30		4:30	
5:00		5:00		5:00		5:00	
5:30		5:30		5:30		5:30	
6:00		6:00		6:00		6:00	
6:30		6:30		6:30		6:30	
7:00		7:00		7:00		7:00	
7:30		7:30		7:30		7:30	
8:00		8:00		8:00		8:00	
8:30		8:30		8:30		8:30	
9:00		9:00		9:00		9:00	
9:30		9:30		9:30		9:30	
10:00		10:00		10:00		10:00	
10:30		10:30		10:30		10:30	
11:00		11:00		11:00		11:00	
	( )		( )		( )		( )

Week of:		Sunday		Monday		Tuesday	
This Week's Goal		S		S		S	
		A		A		A	
		V		V		V	
		E		E		E	
		R		R		R	
		S		S		S	
Intention for the Day		◆		◆		◆	
Grateful for …		◆		◆		◆	

	Sunday	Monday	Tuesday
Start where you are. *Use what you have.* *Do what you can.* —ARTHUR ASHE	5:00	5:00	5:00
	5:30	5:30	5:30
	6:00	6:00	6:00
	6:30	6:30	6:30
	7:00	7:00	7:00
	7:30	7:30	7:30
	8:00	8:00	8:00
	8:30	8:30	8:30
	9:00	9:00	9:00
	9:30	9:30	9:30
TO-DO LIST	10:00	10:00	10:00
Highest Priority	10:30	10:30	10:30
	11:00	11:00	11:00
	11:30	11:30	11:30
	12:00	12:00	12:00
	12:30	12:30	12:30
	1:00	1:00	1:00
Definite Priority	1:30	1:30	1:30
	2:00	2:00	2:00
	2:30	2:30	2:30
	3:00	3:00	3:00
	3:30	3:30	3:30
	4:00	4:00	4:00
Lowest Priority	4:30	4:30	4:30
	5:00	5:00	5:00
	5:30	5:30	5:30
	6:00	6:00	6:00
	6:30	6:30	6:30
	7:00	7:00	7:00
	7:30	7:30	7:30
Habit to Work on This Week	8:00	8:00	8:00
	8:30	8:30	8:30
	9:00	9:00	9:00
	9:30	9:30	9:30
	10:00	10:00	10:00
	10:30	10:30	10:30
	11:00	11:00	11:00

Ready for tomorrow?		( )		( )		( )
ALARM						
CLOTHES						
GLASS OF WATER						
SAVERS PREP						
BEDTIME AFFIRMATIONS						

Wednesday	Thursday	Friday	Saturday
S	S	S	S
A	A	A	A
V	V	V	V
E	E	E	E
R	R	R	R
S	S	S	S
◆	◆	◆	◆
◆	◆	◆	◆

Wednesday		Thursday		Friday		Saturday	
5:00		5:00		5:00		5:00	
5:30		5:30		5:30		5:30	
6:00		6:00		6:00		6:00	
6:30		6:30		6:30		6:30	
7:00		7:00		7:00		7:00	
7:30		7:30		7:30		7:30	
8:00		8:00		8:00		8:00	
8:30		8:30		8:30		8:30	
9:00		9:00		9:00		9:00	
9:30		9:30		9:30		9:30	
10:00		10:00		10:00		10:00	
10:30		10:30		10:30		10:30	
11:00		11:00		11:00		11:00	
11:30		11:30		11:30		11:30	
12:00		12:00		12:00		12:00	
12:30		12:30		12:30		12:30	
1:00		1:00		1:00		1:00	
1:30		1:30		1:30		1:30	
2:00		2:00		2:00		2:00	
2:30		2:30		2:30		2:30	
3:00		3:00		3:00		3:00	
3:30		3:30		3:30		3:30	
4:00		4:00		4:00		4:00	
4:30		4:30		4:30		4:30	
5:00		5:00		5:00		5:00	
5:30		5:30		5:30		5:30	
6:00		6:00		6:00		6:00	
6:30		6:30		6:30		6:30	
7:00		7:00		7:00		7:00	
7:30		7:30		7:30		7:30	
8:00		8:00		8:00		8:00	
8:30		8:30		8:30		8:30	
9:00		9:00		9:00		9:00	
9:30		9:30		9:30		9:30	
10:00		10:00		10:00		10:00	
10:30		10:30		10:30		10:30	
11:00		11:00		11:00		11:00	

( )	( )	( )	( )

MONTHLY REFLECTION

· ·

Write 5 things you accomplished this month:

1.

2.

3.

4.

5.

QUESTIONS

1) What did I learn about myself this month?

2) What tasks are left over from this month that are lingering and need to get done?

3. Did I take care of myself?

4) What could I have done differently this past month?

5) What areas can I (still) improve on?

6) What experiences can I treasure?

7) What challenged me and how did I overcome the challenge?

8) What specific habits and/or rituals could I develop this month to support my vision?

MONTH OF:	SUNDAY	MONDAY	TUESDAY
This Month's Goal			
Important Events or Reminders to Transfer to My Phone			
1.			
2.			
3.			
4.			
5.			
6.			
7.			
8.			
9.			
10.			

PROJECT NAME	TEAM PLAYERS	IMPORTANT DATES	DEADLINES
1.			
2.			
3.			
4.			

WEDNESDAY	THURSDAY	FRIDAY	SATURDAY

BRAINSTORM

Week of:	Sunday		Monday		Tuesday	
This Week's Goal	S		S		S	
	A		A		A	
	V		V		V	
	E		E		E	
	R		R		R	
	S		S		S	
Intention for the Day	◆		◆		◆	
Grateful for …	◆		◆		◆	

Certain things catch your eye, but pursue only those that capture the heart.

—ANCIENT INDIAN PROVERB

TO-DO LIST	Sunday	Monday	Tuesday
Highest Priority	5:00	5:00	5:00
	5:30	5:30	5:30
	6:00	6:00	6:00
	6:30	6:30	6:30
	7:00	7:00	7:00
	7:30	7:30	7:30
	8:00	8:00	8:00
	8:30	8:30	8:30
	9:00	9:00	9:00
	9:30	9:30	9:30
	10:00	10:00	10:00
	10:30	10:30	10:30
	11:00	11:00	11:00
	11:30	11:30	11:30
	12:00	12:00	12:00
	12:30	12:30	12:30
	1:00	1:00	1:00
Definite Priority	1:30	1:30	1:30
	2:00	2:00	2:00
	2:30	2:30	2:30
	3:00	3:00	3:00
	3:30	3:30	3:30
	4:00	4:00	4:00
Lowest Priority	4:30	4:30	4:30
	5:00	5:00	5:00
	5:30	5:30	5:30
	6:00	6:00	6:00
	6:30	6:30	6:30
	7:00	7:00	7:00
	7:30	7:30	7:30
Habit to Work on This Week	8:00	8:00	8:00
	8:30	8:30	8:30
	9:00	9:00	9:00
	9:30	9:30	9:30
	10:00	10:00	10:00
	10:30	10:30	10:30
	11:00	11:00	11:00

Ready for tomorrow?	( )	( )	( )
ALARM			
CLOTHES			
GLASS OF WATER			
SAVERS PREP			
BEDTIME AFFIRMATIONS			

Wednesday		Thursday		Friday		Saturday	
S		S		S		S	
A		A		A		A	
V		V		V		V	
E		E		E		E	
R		R		R		R	
S		S		S		S	
◆		◆		◆		◆	
◆		◆		◆		◆	

Wednesday	Thursday	Friday	Saturday
5:00	5:00	5:00	5:00
5:30	5:30	5:30	5:30
6:00	6:00	6:00	6:00
6:30	6:30	6:30	6:30
7:00	7:00	7:00	7:00
7:30	7:30	7:30	7:30
8:00	8:00	8:00	8:00
8:30	8:30	8:30	8:30
9:00	9:00	9:00	9:00
9:30	9:30	9:30	9:30
10:00	10:00	10:00	10:00
10:30	10:30	10:30	10:30
11:00	11:00	11:00	11:00
11:30	11:30	11:30	11:30
12:00	12:00	12:00	12:00
12:30	12:30	12:30	12:30
1:00	1:00	1:00	1:00
1:30	1:30	1:30	1:30
2:00	2:00	2:00	2:00
2:30	2:30	2:30	2:30
3:00	3:00	3:00	3:00
3:30	3:30	3:30	3:30
4:00	4:00	4:00	4:00
4:30	4:30	4:30	4:30
5:00	5:00	5:00	5:00
5:30	5:30	5:30	5:30
6:00	6:00	6:00	6:00
6:30	6:30	6:30	6:30
7:00	7:00	7:00	7:00
7:30	7:30	7:30	7:30
8:00	8:00	8:00	8:00
8:30	8:30	8:30	8:30
9:00	9:00	9:00	9:00
9:30	9:30	9:30	9:30
10:00	10:00	10:00	10:00
10:30	10:30	10:30	10:30
11:00	11:00	11:00	11:00
( )	( )	( )	( )

Week of:	Sunday	Monday	Tuesday
This Week's Goal	S	S	S
	A	A	A
	V	V	V
	E	E	E
	R	R	R
	S	S	S
Intention for the Day	◆	◆	◆
Grateful for ...	◆	◆	◆

Your success is someone else's miracle.

—JEFF HOFFMAN

TO-DO LIST

Highest Priority

Definite Priority

Lowest Priority

Habit to Work on This Week

Time	Sunday	Monday	Tuesday
5:00			
5:30			
6:00			
6:30			
7:00			
7:30			
8:00			
8:30			
9:00			
9:30			
10:00			
10:30			
11:00			
11:30			
12:00			
12:30			
1:00			
1:30			
2:00			
2:30			
3:00			
3:30			
4:00			
4:30			
5:00			
5:30			
6:00			
6:30			
7:00			
7:30			
8:00			
8:30			
9:00			
9:30			
10:00			
10:30			
11:00			

Ready for tomorrow?	( )	( )	( )
ALARM			
CLOTHES			
GLASS OF WATER			
SAVERS PREP			
BEDTIME AFFIRMATIONS			

Wednesday		Thursday		Friday		Saturday	
S		S		S		S	
A		A		A		A	
V		V		V		V	
E		E		E		E	
R		R		R		R	
S		S		S		S	
◆		◆		◆		◆	
◆		◆		◆		◆	
5:00		5:00		5:00		5:00	
5:30		5:30		5:30		5:30	
6:00		6:00		6:00		6:00	
6:30		6:30		6:30		6:30	
7:00		7:00		7:00		7:00	
7:30		7:30		7:30		7:30	
8:00		8:00		8:00		8:00	
8:30		8:30		8:30		8:30	
9:00		9:00		9:00		9:00	
9:30		9:30		9:30		9:30	
10:00		10:00		10:00		10:00	
10:30		10:30		10:30		10:30	
11:00		11:00		11:00		11:00	
11:30		11:30		11:30		11:30	
12:00		12:00		12:00		12:00	
12:30		12:30		12:30		12:30	
1:00		1:00		1:00		1:00	
1:30		1:30		1:30		1:30	
2:00		2:00		2:00		2:00	
2:30		2:30		2:30		2:30	
3:00		3:00		3:00		3:00	
3:30		3:30		3:30		3:30	
4:00		4:00		4:00		4:00	
4:30		4:30		4:30		4:30	
5:00		5:00		5:00		5:00	
5:30		5:30		5:30		5:30	
6:00		6:00		6:00		6:00	
6:30		6:30		6:30		6:30	
7:00		7:00		7:00		7:00	
7:30		7:30		7:30		7:30	
8:00		8:00		8:00		8:00	
8:30		8:30		8:30		8:30	
9:00		9:00		9:00		9:00	
9:30		9:30		9:30		9:30	
10:00		10:00		10:00		10:00	
10:30		10:30		10:30		10:30	
11:00		11:00		11:00		11:00	
	( )		( )		( )		( )

Week of:	Sunday	Monday	Tuesday
This Week's Goal	S	S	S
	A	A	A
	V	V	V
	E	E	E
	R	R	R
	S	S	S
Intention for the Day	◆	◆	◆
Grateful for ...	◆	◆	◆

Anyone who has never made a mistake has never tried anything new.

—ALBERT EINSTEIN

TO-DO LIST

Highest Priority

Definite Priority

Lowest Priority

Habit to Work on This Week

Time	Sunday	Monday	Tuesday
5:00		5:00	5:00
5:30		5:30	5:30
6:00		6:00	6:00
6:30		6:30	6:30
7:00		7:00	7:00
7:30		7:30	7:30
8:00		8:00	8:00
8:30		8:30	8:30
9:00		9:00	9:00
9:30		9:30	9:30
10:00		10:00	10:00
10:30		10:30	10:30
11:00		11:00	11:00
11:30		11:30	11:30
12:00		12:00	12:00
12:30		12:30	12:30
1:00		1:00	1:00
1:30		1:30	1:30
2:00		2:00	2:00
2:30		2:30	2:30
3:00		3:00	3:00
3:30		3:30	3:30
4:00		4:00	4:00
4:30		4:30	4:30
5:00		5:00	5:00
5:30		5:30	5:30
6:00		6:00	6:00
6:30		6:30	6:30
7:00		7:00	7:00
7:30		7:30	7:30
8:00		8:00	8:00
8:30		8:30	8:30
9:00		9:00	9:00
9:30		9:30	9:30
10:00		10:00	10:00
10:30		10:30	10:30
11:00		11:00	11:00

Ready for tomorrow?	( )	( )	( )
ALARM			
CLOTHES			
GLASS OF WATER			
SAVERS PREP			
BEDTIME AFFIRMATIONS			

Wednesday		Thursday		Friday		Saturday	
S		S		S		S	
A		A		A		A	
V		V		V		V	
E		E		E		E	
R		R		R		R	
S		S		S		S	
◆		◆		◆		◆	
◆		◆		◆		◆	
5:00		5:00		5:00		5:00	
5:30		5:30		5:30		5:30	
6:00		6:00		6:00		6:00	
6:30		6:30		6:30		6:30	
7:00		7:00		7:00		7:00	
7:30		7:30		7:30		7:30	
8:00		8:00		8:00		8:00	
8:30		8:30		8:30		8:30	
9:00		9:00		9:00		9:00	
9:30		9:30		9:30		9:30	
10:00		10:00		10:00		10:00	
10:30		10:30		10:30		10:30	
11:00		11:00		11:00		11:00	
11:30		11:30		11:30		11:30	
12:00		12:00		12:00		12:00	
12:30		12:30		12:30		12:30	
1:00		1:00		1:00		1:00	
1:30		1:30		1:30		1:30	
2:00		2:00		2:00		2:00	
2:30		2:30		2:30		2:30	
3:00		3:00		3:00		3:00	
3:30		3:30		3:30		3:30	
4:00		4:00		4:00		4:00	
4:30		4:30		4:30		4:30	
5:00		5:00		5:00		5:00	
5:30		5:30		5:30		5:30	
6:00		6:00		6:00		6:00	
6:30		6:30		6:30		6:30	
7:00		7:00		7:00		7:00	
7:30		7:30		7:30		7:30	
8:00		8:00		8:00		8:00	
8:30		8:30		8:30		8:30	
9:00		9:00		9:00		9:00	
9:30		9:30		9:30		9:30	
10:00		10:00		10:00		10:00	
10:30		10:30		10:30		10:30	
11:00		11:00		11:00		11:00	
	( )		( )		( )		( )

Week of:	Sunday	Monday	Tuesday
This Week's Goal	S	S	S
	A	A	A
	V	V	V
	E	E	E
	R	R	R
	S	S	S
Intention for the Day	◆	◆	◆
Grateful for ...	◆	◆	◆

Make each day your masterpiece.

—JOHN WOODEN

	Sunday	Monday	Tuesday
	5:00	5:00	5:00
	5:30	5:30	5:30
	6:00	6:00	6:00
	6:30	6:30	6:30
	7:00	7:00	7:00
	7:30	7:30	7:30
	8:00	8:00	8:00
	8:30	8:30	8:30
	9:00	9:00	9:00
	9:30	9:30	9:30
TO-DO LIST	10:00	10:00	10:00
Highest Priority	10:30	10:30	10:30
	11:00	11:00	11:00
	11:30	11:30	11:30
	12:00	12:00	12:00
	12:30	12:30	12:30
	1:00	1:00	1:00
Definite Priority	1:30	1:30	1:30
	2:00	2:00	2:00
	2:30	2:30	2:30
	3:00	3:00	3:00
	3:30	3:30	3:30
	4:00	4:00	4:00
Lowest Priority	4:30	4:30	4:30
	5:00	5:00	5:00
	5:30	5:30	5:30
	6:00	6:00	6:00
	6:30	6:30	6:30
	7:00	7:00	7:00
Habit to Work on This Week	7:30	7:30	7:30
	8:00	8:00	8:00
	8:30	8:30	8:30
	9:00	9:00	9:00
	9:30	9:30	9:30
	10:00	10:00	10:00
	10:30	10:30	10:30
	11:00	11:00	11:00

Ready for tomorrow?	( )	( )	( )
ALARM			
CLOTHES			
GLASS OF WATER			
SAVERS PREP			
BEDTIME AFFIRMATIONS			

Wednesday		Thursday		Friday		Saturday	
S		S		S		S	
A		A		A		A	
V		V		V		V	
E		E		E		E	
R		R		R		R	
S		S		S		S	
◆		◆		◆		◆	
◆		◆		◆		◆	
5:00		5:00		5:00		5:00	
5:30		5:30		5:30		5:30	
6:00		6:00		6:00		6:00	
6:30		6:30		6:30		6:30	
7:00		7:00		7:00		7:00	
7:30		7:30		7:30		7:30	
8:00		8:00		8:00		8:00	
8:30		8:30		8:30		8:30	
9:00		9:00		9:00		9:00	
9:30		9:30		9:30		9:30	
10:00		10:00		10:00		10:00	
10:30		10:30		10:30		10:30	
11:00		11:00		11:00		11:00	
11:30		11:30		11:30		11:30	
12:00		12:00		12:00		12:00	
12:30		12:30		12:30		12:30	
1:00		1:00		1:00		1:00	
1:30		1:30		1:30		1:30	
2:00		2:00		2:00		2:00	
2:30		2:30		2:30		2:30	
3:00		3:00		3:00		3:00	
3:30		3:30		3:30		3:30	
4:00		4:00		4:00		4:00	
4:30		4:30		4:30		4:30	
5:00		5:00		5:00		5:00	
5:30		5:30		5:30		5:30	
6:00		6:00		6:00		6:00	
6:30		6:30		6:30		6:30	
7:00		7:00		7:00		7:00	
7:30		7:30		7:30		7:30	
8:00		8:00		8:00		8:00	
8:30		8:30		8:30		8:30	
9:00		9:00		9:00		9:00	
9:30		9:30		9:30		9:30	
10:00		10:00		10:00		10:00	
10:30		10:30		10:30		10:30	
11:00		11:00		11:00		11:00	
	( )		( )		( )		( )

Week of:		Sunday		Monday		Tuesday	
This Week's Goal		S		S		S	
		A		A		A	
		V		V		V	
		E		E		E	
		R		R		R	
		S		S		S	
Intention for the Day		◆		◆		◆	
Grateful for ...		◆		◆		◆	

To avoid criticism, do nothing, say nothing, be nothing.

—ELBERT HUBBARD

TO-DO LIST		Sunday		Monday		Tuesday	
Highest Priority		5:00		5:00		5:00	
		5:30		5:30		5:30	
		6:00		6:00		6:00	
		6:30		6:30		6:30	
		7:00		7:00		7:00	
		7:30		7:30		7:30	
		8:00		8:00		8:00	
		8:30		8:30		8:30	
		9:00		9:00		9:00	
		9:30		9:30		9:30	
		10:00		10:00		10:00	
		10:30		10:30		10:30	
		11:00		11:00		11:00	
		11:30		11:30		11:30	
		12:00		12:00		12:00	
		12:30		12:30		12:30	
		1:00		1:00		1:00	
Definite Priority		1:30		1:30		1:30	
		2:00		2:00		2:00	
		2:30		2:30		2:30	
		3:00		3:00		3:00	
		3:30		3:30		3:30	
		4:00		4:00		4:00	
Lowest Priority		4:30		4:30		4:30	
		5:00		5:00		5:00	
		5:30		5:30		5:30	
		6:00		6:00		6:00	
		6:30		6:30		6:30	
		7:00		7:00		7:00	
		7:30		7:30		7:30	
Habit to Work on This Week		8:00		8:00		8:00	
		8:30		8:30		8:30	
		9:00		9:00		9:00	
		9:30		9:30		9:30	
		10:00		10:00		10:00	
		10:30		10:30		10:30	
		11:00		11:00		11:00	

Ready for tomorrow?	( )	( )	( )
ALARM			
CLOTHES			
GLASS OF WATER			
SAVERS PREP			
BEDTIME AFFIRMATIONS			

Wednesday	Thursday	Friday	Saturday
S	S	S	S
A	A	A	A
V	V	V	V
E	E	E	E
R	R	R	R
S	S	S	S

◆	◆	◆	◆
◆	◆	◆	◆

Wednesday		Thursday		Friday		Saturday	
5:00		5:00		5:00		5:00	
5:30		5:30		5:30		5:30	
6:00		6:00		6:00		6:00	
6:30		6:30		6:30		6:30	
7:00		7:00		7:00		7:00	
7:30		7:30		7:30		7:30	
8:00		8:00		8:00		8:00	
8:30		8:30		8:30		8:30	
9:00		9:00		9:00		9:00	
9:30		9:30		9:30		9:30	
10:00		10:00		10:00		10:00	
10:30		10:30		10:30		10:30	
11:00		11:00		11:00		11:00	
11:30		11:30		11:30		11:30	
12:00		12:00		12:00		12:00	
12:30		12:30		12:30		12:30	
1:00		1:00		1:00		1:00	
1:30		1:30		1:30		1:30	
2:00		2:00		2:00		2:00	
2:30		2:30		2:30		2:30	
3:00		3:00		3:00		3:00	
3:30		3:30		3:30		3:30	
4:00		4:00		4:00		4:00	
4:30		4:30		4:30		4:30	
5:00		5:00		5:00		5:00	
5:30		5:30		5:30		5:30	
6:00		6:00		6:00		6:00	
6:30		6:30		6:30		6:30	
7:00		7:00		7:00		7:00	
7:30		7:30		7:30		7:30	
8:00		8:00		8:00		8:00	
8:30		8:30		8:30		8:30	
9:00		9:00		9:00		9:00	
9:30		9:30		9:30		9:30	
10:00		10:00		10:00		10:00	
10:30		10:30		10:30		10:30	
11:00		11:00		11:00		11:00	

( )	( )	( )	( )

MONTHLY REFLECTION

....

Write 5 things you accomplished this month:

1.

2.

3.

4.

5.

QUESTIONS

1) What did I learn about myself this month?

2) What tasks are left over from this month that are lingering and need to get done?

3. Did I take care of myself?

4) What could I have done differently this past month?

5) What areas can I (still) improve on?

6) What experiences can I treasure?

7) What challenged me and how did I overcome the challenge?

8) What specific habits and/or rituals could I develop this month to support my vision?

MONTH OF:	SUNDAY	MONDAY	TUESDAY
This Month's Goal			
Important Events or Reminders to Transfer to My Phone			
1.			
2.			
3.			
4.			
5.			
6.			
7.			
8.			
9.			
10.			

PROJECT NAME	TEAM PLAYERS	IMPORTANT DATES	DEADLINES
1.			
2.			
3.			
4.			

WEDNESDAY	THURSDAY	FRIDAY	SATURDAY

BRAINSTORM

Week of:	Sunday	Monday	Tuesday
This Week's Goal	S	S	S
	A	A	A
	V	V	V
	E	E	E
	R	R	R
	S	S	S
Intention for the Day	◆	◆	◆
Grateful for ...	◆	◆	◆

It's not whether you get knocked down, it's whether you get up.

—VINCE LOMBARDI

TO-DO LIST

Highest Priority

Definite Priority

Lowest Priority

Habit to Work on This Week

	Sunday	Monday	Tuesday
5:00		5:00		5:00	
5:30		5:30		5:30	
6:00		6:00		6:00	
6:30		6:30		6:30	
7:00		7:00		7:00	
7:30		7:30		7:30	
8:00		8:00		8:00	
8:30		8:30		8:30	
9:00		9:00		9:00	
9:30		9:30		9:30	
10:00		10:00		10:00	
10:30		10:30		10:30	
11:00		11:00		11:00	
11:30		11:30		11:30	
12:00		12:00		12:00	
12:30		12:30		12:30	
1:00		1:00		1:00	
1:30		1:30		1:30	
2:00		2:00		2:00	
2:30		2:30		2:30	
3:00		3:00		3:00	
3:30		3:30		3:30	
4:00		4:00		4:00	
4:30		4:30		4:30	
5:00		5:00		5:00	
5:30		5:30		5:30	
6:00		6:00		6:00	
6:30		6:30		6:30	
7:00		7:00		7:00	
7:30		7:30		7:30	
8:00		8:00		8:00	
8:30		8:30		8:30	
9:00		9:00		9:00	
9:30		9:30		9:30	
10:00		10:00		10:00	
10:30		10:30		10:30	
11:00		11:00		11:00	

Ready for tomorrow?	( )	( )	( )
ALARM			
CLOTHES			
GLASS OF WATER			
SAVERS PREP			
BEDTIME AFFIRMATIONS			

Wednesday		Thursday		Friday		Saturday	
S		S		S		S	
A		A		A		A	
V		V		V		V	
E		E		E		E	
R		R		R		R	
S		S		S		S	
◆		◆		◆		◆	
◆		◆		◆		◆	
5:00		5:00		5:00		5:00	
5:30		5:30		5:30		5:30	
6:00		6:00		6:00		6:00	
6:30		6:30		6:30		6:30	
7:00		7:00		7:00		7:00	
7:30		7:30		7:30		7:30	
8:00		8:00		8:00		8:00	
8:30		8:30		8:30		8:30	
9:00		9:00		9:00		9:00	
9:30		9:30		9:30		9:30	
10:00		10:00		10:00		10:00	
10:30		10:30		10:30		10:30	
11:00		11:00		11:00		11:00	
11:30		11:30		11:30		11:30	
12:00		12:00		12:00		12:00	
12:30		12:30		12:30		12:30	
1:00		1:00		1:00		1:00	
1:30		1:30		1:30		1:30	
2:00		2:00		2:00		2:00	
2:30		2:30		2:30		2:30	
3:00		3:00		3:00		3:00	
3:30		3:30		3:30		3:30	
4:00		4:00		4:00		4:00	
4:30		4:30		4:30		4:30	
5:00		5:00		5:00		5:00	
5:30		5:30		5:30		5:30	
6:00		6:00		6:00		6:00	
6:30		6:30		6:30		6:30	
7:00		7:00		7:00		7:00	
7:30		7:30		7:30		7:30	
8:00		8:00		8:00		8:00	
8:30		8:30		8:30		8:30	
9:00		9:00		9:00		9:00	
9:30		9:30		9:30		9:30	
10:00		10:00		10:00		10:00	
10:30		10:30		10:30		10:30	
11:00		11:00		11:00		11:00	
( )		( )		( )		( )	

Week of:	Sunday	Monday	Tuesday
This Week's Goal	S	S	S
	A	A	A
	V	V	V
	E	E	E
	R	R	R
	S	S	S
Intention for the Day	◆	◆	◆
Grateful for ...	◆	◆	◆

There is nothing to fear, because you cannot fail— only learn, grow, and become better than you've ever been before.

—HAL ELROD

TO-DO LIST

Highest Priority

Definite Priority

Lowest Priority

Habit to Work on This Week

Time	Sunday	Time	Monday	Time	Tuesday
5:00		5:00		5:00	
5:30		5:30		5:30	
6:00		6:00		6:00	
6:30		6:30		6:30	
7:00		7:00		7:00	
7:30		7:30		7:30	
8:00		8:00		8:00	
8:30		8:30		8:30	
9:00		9:00		9:00	
9:30		9:30		9:30	
10:00		10:00		10:00	
10:30		10:30		10:30	
11:00		11:00		11:00	
11:30		11:30		11:30	
12:00		12:00		12:00	
12:30		12:30		12:30	
1:00		1:00		1:00	
1:30		1:30		1:30	
2:00		2:00		2:00	
2:30		2:30		2:30	
3:00		3:00		3:00	
3:30		3:30		3:30	
4:00		4:00		4:00	
4:30		4:30		4:30	
5:00		5:00		5:00	
5:30		5:30		5:30	
6:00		6:00		6:00	
6:30		6:30		6:30	
7:00		7:00		7:00	
7:30		7:30		7:30	
8:00		8:00		8:00	
8:30		8:30		8:30	
9:00		9:00		9:00	
9:30		9:30		9:30	
10:00		10:00		10:00	
10:30		10:30		10:30	
11:00		11:00		11:00	

Ready for tomorrow?	( )	( )	( )
ALARM			
CLOTHES			
GLASS OF WATER			
SAVERS PREP			
BEDTIME AFFIRMATIONS			

Wednesday	Thursday	Friday	Saturday
S	S	S	S
A	A	A	A
V	V	V	V
E	E	E	E
R	R	R	R
S	S	S	S
◆	◆	◆	◆
◆	◆	◆	◆

Wednesday		Thursday		Friday		Saturday	
5:00		5:00		5:00		5:00	
5:30		5:30		5:30		5:30	
6:00		6:00		6:00		6:00	
6:30		6:30		6:30		6:30	
7:00		7:00		7:00		7:00	
7:30		7:30		7:30		7:30	
8:00		8:00		8:00		8:00	
8:30		8:30		8:30		8:30	
9:00		9:00		9:00		9:00	
9:30		9:30		9:30		9:30	
10:00		10:00		10:00		10:00	
10:30		10:30		10:30		10:30	
11:00		11:00		11:00		11:00	
11:30		11:30		11:30		11:30	
12:00		12:00		12:00		12:00	
12:30		12:30		12:30		12:30	
1:00		1:00		1:00		1:00	
1:30		1:30		1:30		1:30	
2:00		2:00		2:00		2:00	
2:30		2:30		2:30		2:30	
3:00		3:00		3:00		3:00	
3:30		3:30		3:30		3:30	
4:00		4:00		4:00		4:00	
4:30		4:30		4:30		4:30	
5:00		5:00		5:00		5:00	
5:30		5:30		5:30		5:30	
6:00		6:00		6:00		6:00	
6:30		6:30		6:30		6:30	
7:00		7:00		7:00		7:00	
7:30		7:30		7:30		7:30	
8:00		8:00		8:00		8:00	
8:30		8:30		8:30		8:30	
9:00		9:00		9:00		9:00	
9:30		9:30		9:30		9:30	
10:00		10:00		10:00		10:00	
10:30		10:30		10:30		10:30	
11:00		11:00		11:00		11:00	

( )	( )	( )	( )

Week of:	Sunday		Monday		Tuesday	
This Week's Goal	S		S		S	
	A		A		A	
	V		V		V	
	E		E		E	
	R		R		R	
	S		S		S	
Intention for the Day	◆		◆		◆	
Grateful for ...	◆		◆		◆	

The harder I work, the luckier I get.

—GARY PLAYER

TO-DO LIST		Sunday		Monday		Tuesday
Highest Priority	5:00		5:00		5:00	
	5:30		5:30		5:30	
	6:00		6:00		6:00	
	6:30		6:30		6:30	
	7:00		7:00		7:00	
	7:30		7:30		7:30	
	8:00		8:00		8:00	
	8:30		8:30		8:30	
	9:00		9:00		9:00	
	9:30		9:30		9:30	
	10:00		10:00		10:00	
	10:30		10:30		10:30	
	11:00		11:00		11:00	
	11:30		11:30		11:30	
	12:00		12:00		12:00	
	12:30		12:30		12:30	
	1:00		1:00		1:00	
Definite Priority	1:30		1:30		1:30	
	2:00		2:00		2:00	
	2:30		2:30		2:30	
	3:00		3:00		3:00	
	3:30		3:30		3:30	
	4:00		4:00		4:00	
Lowest Priority	4:30		4:30		4:30	
	5:00		5:00		5:00	
	5:30		5:30		5:30	
	6:00		6:00		6:00	
	6:30		6:30		6:30	
	7:00		7:00		7:00	
	7:30		7:30		7:30	
Habit to Work on This Week	8:00		8:00		8:00	
	8:30		8:30		8:30	
	9:00		9:00		9:00	
	9:30		9:30		9:30	
	10:00		10:00		10:00	
	10:30		10:30		10:30	
	11:00		11:00		11:00	

Ready for tomorrow?	( )	( )	( )
ALARM			
CLOTHES			
GLASS OF WATER			
SAVERS PREP			
BEDTIME AFFIRMATIONS			

Wednesday		Thursday		Friday		Saturday	
S		S		S		S	
A		A		A		A	
V		V		V		V	
E		E		E		E	
R		R		R		R	
S		S		S		S	
◆		◆		◆		◆	
◆		◆		◆		◆	
5:00		5:00		5:00		5:00	
5:30		5:30		5:30		5:30	
6:00		6:00		6:00		6:00	
6:30		6:30		6:30		6:30	
7:00		7:00		7:00		7:00	
7:30		7:30		7:30		7:30	
8:00		8:00		8:00		8:00	
8:30		8:30		8:30		8:30	
9:00		9:00		9:00		9:00	
9:30		9:30		9:30		9:30	
10:00		10:00		10:00		10:00	
10:30		10:30		10:30		10:30	
11:00		11:00		11:00		11:00	
11:30		11:30		11:30		11:30	
12:00		12:00		12:00		12:00	
12:30		12:30		12:30		12:30	
1:00		1:00		1:00		1:00	
1:30		1:30		1:30		1:30	
2:00		2:00		2:00		2:00	
2:30		2:30		2:30		2:30	
3:00		3:00		3:00		3:00	
3:30		3:30		3:30		3:30	
4:00		4:00		4:00		4:00	
4:30		4:30		4:30		4:30	
5:00		5:00		5:00		5:00	
5:30		5:30		5:30		5:30	
6:00		6:00		6:00		6:00	
6:30		6:30		6:30		6:30	
7:00		7:00		7:00		7:00	
7:30		7:30		7:30		7:30	
8:00		8:00		8:00		8:00	
8:30		8:30		8:30		8:30	
9:00		9:00		9:00		9:00	
9:30		9:30		9:30		9:30	
10:00		10:00		10:00		10:00	
10:30		10:30		10:30		10:30	
11:00		11:00		11:00		11:00	
	( )		( )		( )		( )

Week of:	Sunday		Monday		Tuesday	
This Week's Goal	S		S		S	
	A		A		A	
	V		V		V	
	E		E		E	
	R		R		R	
	S		S		S	
Intention for the Day	◆		◆		◆	
Grateful for …	◆		◆		◆	

Either you run the day, or the day runs you.

—JIM ROHN

TO-DO LIST		Sunday		Monday		Tuesday
Highest Priority	5:00		5:00		5:00	
	5:30		5:30		5:30	
	6:00		6:00		6:00	
	6:30		6:30		6:30	
	7:00		7:00		7:00	
	7:30		7:30		7:30	
	8:00		8:00		8:00	
	8:30		8:30		8:30	
	9:00		9:00		9:00	
	9:30		9:30		9:30	
	10:00		10:00		10:00	
	10:30		10:30		10:30	
	11:00		11:00		11:00	
	11:30		11:30		11:30	
	12:00		12:00		12:00	
	12:30		12:30		12:30	
	1:00		1:00		1:00	
Definite Priority	1:30		1:30		1:30	
	2:00		2:00		2:00	
	2:30		2:30		2:30	
	3:00		3:00		3:00	
	3:30		3:30		3:30	
	4:00		4:00		4:00	
Lowest Priority	4:30		4:30		4:30	
	5:00		5:00		5:00	
	5:30		5:30		5:30	
	6:00		6:00		6:00	
	6:30		6:30		6:30	
	7:00		7:00		7:00	
	7:30		7:30		7:30	
Habit to Work on This Week	8:00		8:00		8:00	
	8:30		8:30		8:30	
	9:00		9:00		9:00	
	9:30		9:30		9:30	
	10:00		10:00		10:00	
	10:30		10:30		10:30	
	11:00		11:00		11:00	

Ready for tomorrow?	( )	( )	( )
ALARM			
CLOTHES			
GLASS OF WATER			
SAVERS PREP			
BEDTIME AFFIRMATIONS			

Wednesday	Thursday	Friday	Saturday
S	S	S	S
A	A	A	A
V	V	V	V
E	E	E	E
R	R	R	R
S	S	S	S

◆	◆	◆	◆
◆	◆	◆	◆

Wednesday		Thursday		Friday		Saturday	
5:00		5:00		5:00		5:00	
5:30		5:30		5:30		5:30	
6:00		6:00		6:00		6:00	
6:30		6:30		6:30		6:30	
7:00		7:00		7:00		7:00	
7:30		7:30		7:30		7:30	
8:00		8:00		8:00		8:00	
8:30		8:30		8:30		8:30	
9:00		9:00		9:00		9:00	
9:30		9:30		9:30		9:30	
10:00		10:00		10:00		10:00	
10:30		10:30		10:30		10:30	
11:00		11:00		11:00		11:00	
11:30		11:30		11:30		11:30	
12:00		12:00		12:00		12:00	
12:30		12:30		12:30		12:30	
1:00		1:00		1:00		1:00	
1:30		1:30		1:30		1:30	
2:00		2:00		2:00		2:00	
2:30		2:30		2:30		2:30	
3:00		3:00		3:00		3:00	
3:30		3:30		3:30		3:30	
4:00		4:00		4:00		4:00	
4:30		4:30		4:30		4:30	
5:00		5:00		5:00		5:00	
5:30		5:30		5:30		5:30	
6:00		6:00		6:00		6:00	
6:30		6:30		6:30		6:30	
7:00		7:00		7:00		7:00	
7:30		7:30		7:30		7:30	
8:00		8:00		8:00		8:00	
8:30		8:30		8:30		8:30	
9:00		9:00		9:00		9:00	
9:30		9:30		9:30		9:30	
10:00		10:00		10:00		10:00	
10:30		10:30		10:30		10:30	
11:00		11:00		11:00		11:00	
( )		( )		( )		( )	

Week of:	Sunday	Monday	Tuesday
This Week's Goal	S	S	S
	A	A	A
	V	V	V
	E	E	E
	R	R	R
	S	S	S
Intention for the Day	◆	◆	◆
Grateful for ...	◆	◆	◆

Change your thoughts and you change your world.

—NORMAN VINCENT PEALE

TO-DO LIST	Sunday	Monday	Tuesday
Highest Priority	5:00	5:00	5:00
	5:30	5:30	5:30
	6:00	6:00	6:00
	6:30	6:30	6:30
	7:00	7:00	7:00
	7:30	7:30	7:30
	8:00	8:00	8:00
	8:30	8:30	8:30
	9:00	9:00	9:00
	9:30	9:30	9:30
	10:00	10:00	10:00
	10:30	10:30	10:30
	11:00	11:00	11:00
	11:30	11:30	11:30
	12:00	12:00	12:00
	12:30	12:30	12:30
	1:00	1:00	1:00
Definite Priority	1:30	1:30	1:30
	2:00	2:00	2:00
	2:30	2:30	2:30
	3:00	3:00	3:00
	3:30	3:30	3:30
	4:00	4:00	4:00
Lowest Priority	4:30	4:30	4:30
	5:00	5:00	5:00
	5:30	5:30	5:30
	6:00	6:00	6:00
	6:30	6:30	6:30
	7:00	7:00	7:00
Habit to Work on This Week	7:30	7:30	7:30
	8:00	8:00	8:00
	8:30	8:30	8:30
	9:00	9:00	9:00
	9:30	9:30	9:30
	10:00	10:00	10:00
	10:30	10:30	10:30
	11:00	11:00	11:00

Ready for tomorrow?	( )	( )	( )
ALARM			
CLOTHES			
GLASS OF WATER			
SAVERS PREP			
BEDTIME AFFIRMATIONS			

Wednesday		Thursday		Friday		Saturday	
S		S		S		S	
A		A		A		A	
V		V		V		V	
E		E		E		E	
R		R		R		R	
S		S		S		S	
◆		◆		◆		◆	
◆		◆		◆		◆	
5:00		5:00		5:00		5:00	
5:30		5:30		5:30		5:30	
6:00		6:00		6:00		6:00	
6:30		6:30		6:30		6:30	
7:00		7:00		7:00		7:00	
7:30		7:30		7:30		7:30	
8:00		8:00		8:00		8:00	
8:30		8:30		8:30		8:30	
9:00		9:00		9:00		9:00	
9:30		9:30		9:30		9:30	
10:00		10:00		10:00		10:00	
10:30		10:30		10:30		10:30	
11:00		11:00		11:00		11:00	
11:30		11:30		11:30		11:30	
12:00		12:00		12:00		12:00	
12:30		12:30		12:30		12:30	
1:00		1:00		1:00		1:00	
1:30		1:30		1:30		1:30	
2:00		2:00		2:00		2:00	
2:30		2:30		2:30		2:30	
3:00		3:00		3:00		3:00	
3:30		3:30		3:30		3:30	
4:00		4:00		4:00		4:00	
4:30		4:30		4:30		4:30	
5:00		5:00		5:00		5:00	
5:30		5:30		5:30		5:30	
6:00		6:00		6:00		6:00	
6:30		6:30		6:30		6:30	
7:00		7:00		7:00		7:00	
7:30		7:30		7:30		7:30	
8:00		8:00		8:00		8:00	
8:30		8:30		8:30		8:30	
9:00		9:00		9:00		9:00	
9:30		9:30		9:30		9:30	
10:00		10:00		10:00		10:00	
10:30		10:30		10:30		10:30	
11:00		11:00		11:00		11:00	
( )		( )		( )		( )	

MONTHLY REFLECTION

● ●

Write 5 things you accomplished this month:

1.

2.

3.

4.

5.

QUESTIONS

1) What did I learn about myself this month?

2) What tasks are left over from this month that are lingering and need to get done?

3. Did I take care of myself?

4) What could I have done differently this past month?

5) What areas can I (still) improve on?

6) What experiences can I treasure?

7) What challenged me and how did I overcome the challenge?

8) What specific habits and/or rituals could I develop this month to support my vision?

MONTH OF:	SUNDAY	MONDAY	TUESDAY
This Month's Goal			
Important Events or Reminders to Transfer to My Phone			
1.			
2.			
3.			
4.			
5.			
6.			
7.			
8.			
9.			
10.			

PROJECT NAME	TEAM PLAYERS	IMPORTANT DATES	DEADLINES
1.			
2.			
3.			
4.			

WEDNESDAY	THURSDAY	FRIDAY	SATURDAY

BRAINSTORM

Week of:	Sunday		Monday		Tuesday	
This Week's Goal	S		S		S	
	A		A		A	
	V		V		V	
	E		E		E	
	R		R		R	
	S		S		S	
Intention for the Day	◆		◆		◆	
Grateful for ...	◆		◆		◆	

	Sunday	Monday	Tuesday
	5:00	5:00	5:00
	5:30	5:30	5:30
Someday is not a day of the week. —DENISE BRENNAN-NELSON	6:00	6:00	6:00
	6:30	6:30	6:30
	7:00	7:00	7:00
	7:30	7:30	7:30
	8:00	8:00	8:00
	8:30	8:30	8:30
	9:00	9:00	9:00
	9:30	9:30	9:30
TO-DO LIST	10:00	10:00	10:00
Highest Priority	10:30	10:30	10:30
	11:00	11:00	11:00
	11:30	11:30	11:30
	12:00	12:00	12:00
	12:30	12:30	12:30
	1:00	1:00	1:00
Definite Priority	1:30	1:30	1:30
	2:00	2:00	2:00
	2:30	2:30	2:30
	3:00	3:00	3:00
	3:30	3:30	3:30
	4:00	4:00	4:00
Lowest Priority	4:30	4:30	4:30
	5:00	5:00	5:00
	5:30	5:30	5:30
	6:00	6:00	6:00
	6:30	6:30	6:30
	7:00	7:00	7:00
	7:30	7:30	7:30
Habit to Work on This Week	8:00	8:00	8:00
	8:30	8:30	8:30
	9:00	9:00	9:00
	9:30	9:30	9:30
	10:00	10:00	10:00
	10:30	10:30	10:30
	11:00	11:00	11:00

Ready for tomorrow?	( )	( )	( )
ALARM			
CLOTHES			
GLASS OF WATER			
SAVERS PREP			
BEDTIME AFFIRMATIONS			

Wednesday		Thursday		Friday		Saturday	
S		S		S		S	
A		A		A		A	
V		V		V		V	
E		E		E		E	
R		R		R		R	
S		S		S		S	
◆		◆		◆		◆	
◆		◆		◆		◆	
5:00		5:00		5:00		5:00	
5:30		5:30		5:30		5:30	
6:00		6:00		6:00		6:00	
6:30		6:30		6:30		6:30	
7:00		7:00		7:00		7:00	
7:30		7:30		7:30		7:30	
8:00		8:00		8:00		8:00	
8:30		8:30		8:30		8:30	
9:00		9:00		9:00		9:00	
9:30		9:30		9:30		9:30	
10:00		10:00		10:00		10:00	
10:30		10:30		10:30		10:30	
11:00		11:00		11:00		11:00	
11:30		11:30		11:30		11:30	
12:00		12:00		12:00		12:00	
12:30		12:30		12:30		12:30	
1:00		1:00		1:00		1:00	
1:30		1:30		1:30		1:30	
2:00		2:00		2:00		2:00	
2:30		2:30		2:30		2:30	
3:00		3:00		3:00		3:00	
3:30		3:30		3:30		3:30	
4:00		4:00		4:00		4:00	
4:30		4:30		4:30		4:30	
5:00		5:00		5:00		5:00	
5:30		5:30		5:30		5:30	
6:00		6:00		6:00		6:00	
6:30		6:30		6:30		6:30	
7:00		7:00		7:00		7:00	
7:30		7:30		7:30		7:30	
8:00		8:00		8:00		8:00	
8:30		8:30		8:30		8:30	
9:00		9:00		9:00		9:00	
9:30		9:30		9:30		9:30	
10:00		10:00		10:00		10:00	
10:30		10:30		10:30		10:30	
11:00		11:00		11:00		11:00	
	( )		( )		( )		( )

Week of:	Sunday	Monday	Tuesday
This Week's Goal	S	S	S
	A	A	A
	V	V	V
	E	E	E
	R	R	R
	S	S	S
Intention for the Day	◆	◆	◆
Grateful for ...	◆	◆	◆

> *The journey of a thousand miles begins with one step.*
>
> —LAO TZU

TO-DO LIST	Sunday	Monday	Tuesday
Highest Priority	5:00	5:00	5:00
	5:30	5:30	5:30
	6:00	6:00	6:00
	6:30	6:30	6:30
	7:00	7:00	7:00
	7:30	7:30	7:30
	8:00	8:00	8:00
	8:30	8:30	8:30
	9:00	9:00	9:00
	9:30	9:30	9:30
	10:00	10:00	10:00
	10:30	10:30	10:30
	11:00	11:00	11:00
	11:30	11:30	11:30
	12:00	12:00	12:00
	12:30	12:30	12:30
	1:00	1:00	1:00
Definite Priority	1:30	1:30	1:30
	2:00	2:00	2:00
	2:30	2:30	2:30
	3:00	3:00	3:00
	3:30	3:30	3:30
	4:00	4:00	4:00
Lowest Priority	4:30	4:30	4:30
	5:00	5:00	5:00
	5:30	5:30	5:30
	6:00	6:00	6:00
	6:30	6:30	6:30
	7:00	7:00	7:00
	7:30	7:30	7:30
Habit to Work on This Week	8:00	8:00	8:00
	8:30	8:30	8:30
	9:00	9:00	9:00
	9:30	9:30	9:30
	10:00	10:00	10:00
	10:30	10:30	10:30
	11:00	11:00	11:00

Ready for tomorrow?	( )	( )	( )
ALARM			
CLOTHES			
GLASS OF WATER			
SAVERS PREP			
BEDTIME AFFIRMATIONS			

Wednesday	Thursday	Friday	Saturday
S	S	S	S
A	A	A	A
V	V	V	V
E	E	E	E
R	R	R	R
S	S	S	S

◆	◆	◆	◆
◆	◆	◆	◆

	Wednesday		Thursday		Friday		Saturday
5:00		5:00		5:00		5:00	
5:30		5:30		5:30		5:30	
6:00		6:00		6:00		6:00	
6:30		6:30		6:30		6:30	
7:00		7:00		7:00		7:00	
7:30		7:30		7:30		7:30	
8:00		8:00		8:00		8:00	
8:30		8:30		8:30		8:30	
9:00		9:00		9:00		9:00	
9:30		9:30		9:30		9:30	
10:00		10:00		10:00		10:00	
10:30		10:30		10:30		10:30	
11:00		11:00		11:00		11:00	
11:30		11:30		11:30		11:30	
12:00		12:00		12:00		12:00	
12:30		12:30		12:30		12:30	
1:00		1:00		1:00		1:00	
1:30		1:30		1:30		1:30	
2:00		2:00		2:00		2:00	
2:30		2:30		2:30		2:30	
3:00		3:00		3:00		3:00	
3:30		3:30		3:30		3:30	
4:00		4:00		4:00		4:00	
4:30		4:30		4:30		4:30	
5:00		5:00		5:00		5:00	
5:30		5:30		5:30		5:30	
6:00		6:00		6:00		6:00	
6:30		6:30		6:30		6:30	
7:00		7:00		7:00		7:00	
7:30		7:30		7:30		7:30	
8:00		8:00		8:00		8:00	
8:30		8:30		8:30		8:30	
9:00		9:00		9:00		9:00	
9:30		9:30		9:30		9:30	
10:00		10:00		10:00		10:00	
10:30		10:30		10:30		10:30	
11:00		11:00		11:00		11:00	

( )	( )	( )	( )

Week of:	Sunday		Monday		Tuesday	
This Week's Goal	S		S		S	
	A		A		A	
	V		V		V	
	E		E		E	
	R		R		R	
	S		S		S	
Intention for the Day	◆		◆		◆	
Grateful for ...	◆		◆		◆	

Kindness is the language which the deaf can hear and the blind can see.

—**MARK TWAIN**

TO-DO LIST

Highest Priority

Definite Priority

Lowest Priority

Habit to Work on This Week

Time	Sunday	Monday	Tuesday
5:00			
5:30			
6:00			
6:30			
7:00			
7:30			
8:00			
8:30			
9:00			
9:30			
10:00			
10:30			
11:00			
11:30			
12:00			
12:30			
1:00			
1:30			
2:00			
2:30			
3:00			
3:30			
4:00			
4:30			
5:00			
5:30			
6:00			
6:30			
7:00			
7:30			
8:00			
8:30			
9:00			
9:30			
10:00			
10:30			
11:00			

Ready for tomorrow?	( )	( )	( )
ALARM			
CLOTHES			
GLASS OF WATER			
SAVERS PREP			
BEDTIME AFFIRMATIONS			

Wednesday	Thursday	Friday	Saturday
S	S	S	S
A	A	A	A
V	V	V	V
E	E	E	E
R	R	R	R
S	S	S	S
◆	◆	◆	◆
◆	◆	◆	◆

	Wednesday		Thursday		Friday		Saturday
5:00		5:00		5:00		5:00	
5:30		5:30		5:30		5:30	
6:00		6:00		6:00		6:00	
6:30		6:30		6:30		6:30	
7:00		7:00		7:00		7:00	
7:30		7:30		7:30		7:30	
8:00		8:00		8:00		8:00	
8:30		8:30		8:30		8:30	
9:00		9:00		9:00		9:00	
9:30		9:30		9:30		9:30	
10:00		10:00		10:00		10:00	
10:30		10:30		10:30		10:30	
11:00		11:00		11:00		11:00	
11:30		11:30		11:30		11:30	
12:00		12:00		12:00		12:00	
12:30		12:30		12:30		12:30	
1:00		1:00		1:00		1:00	
1:30		1:30		1:30		1:30	
2:00		2:00		2:00		2:00	
2:30		2:30		2:30		2:30	
3:00		3:00		3:00		3:00	
3:30		3:30		3:30		3:30	
4:00		4:00		4:00		4:00	
4:30		4:30		4:30		4:30	
5:00		5:00		5:00		5:00	
5:30		5:30		5:30		5:30	
6:00		6:00		6:00		6:00	
6:30		6:30		6:30		6:30	
7:00		7:00		7:00		7:00	
7:30		7:30		7:30		7:30	
8:00		8:00		8:00		8:00	
8:30		8:30		8:30		8:30	
9:00		9:00		9:00		9:00	
9:30		9:30		9:30		9:30	
10:00		10:00		10:00		10:00	
10:30		10:30		10:30		10:30	
11:00		11:00		11:00		11:00	
	( )		( )		( )		( )

Week of:	Sunday	Monday	Tuesday
This Week's Goal	S	S	S
	A	A	A
	V	V	V
	E	E	E
	R	R	R
	S	S	S
Intention for the Day	◆	◆	◆
Grateful for ...	◆	◆	◆

The body heals with play, the mind heals with laughter, and the spirit heals with joy.

—PROVERB

TO-DO LIST
Highest Priority
Definite Priority
Lowest Priority
Habit to Work on This Week

Time	Sunday	Monday	Tuesday
5:00			
5:30			
6:00			
6:30			
7:00			
7:30			
8:00			
8:30			
9:00			
9:30			
10:00			
10:30			
11:00			
11:30			
12:00			
12:30			
1:00			
1:30			
2:00			
2:30			
3:00			
3:30			
4:00			
4:30			
5:00			
5:30			
6:00			
6:30			
7:00			
7:30			
8:00			
8:30			
9:00			
9:30			
10:00			
10:30			
11:00			

Ready for tomorrow?	( )	( )	( )
ALARM			
CLOTHES			
GLASS OF WATER			
SAVERS PREP			
BEDTIME AFFIRMATIONS			

Wednesday	Thursday	Friday	Saturday
S	S	S	S
A	A	A	A
V	V	V	V
E	E	E	E
R	R	R	R
S	S	S	S
◆	◆	◆	◆
◆	◆	◆	◆

Wednesday		Thursday		Friday		Saturday	
5:00		5:00		5:00		5:00	
5:30		5:30		5:30		5:30	
6:00		6:00		6:00		6:00	
6:30		6:30		6:30		6:30	
7:00		7:00		7:00		7:00	
7:30		7:30		7:30		7:30	
8:00		8:00		8:00		8:00	
8:30		8:30		8:30		8:30	
9:00		9:00		9:00		9:00	
9:30		9:30		9:30		9:30	
10:00		10:00		10:00		10:00	
10:30		10:30		10:30		10:30	
11:00		11:00		11:00		11:00	
11:30		11:30		11:30		11:30	
12:00		12:00		12:00		12:00	
12:30		12:30		12:30		12:30	
1:00		1:00		1:00		1:00	
1:30		1:30		1:30		1:30	
2:00		2:00		2:00		2:00	
2:30		2:30		2:30		2:30	
3:00		3:00		3:00		3:00	
3:30		3:30		3:30		3:30	
4:00		4:00		4:00		4:00	
4:30		4:30		4:30		4:30	
5:00		5:00		5:00		5:00	
5:30		5:30		5:30		5:30	
6:00		6:00		6:00		6:00	
6:30		6:30		6:30		6:30	
7:00		7:00		7:00		7:00	
7:30		7:30		7:30		7:30	
8:00		8:00		8:00		8:00	
8:30		8:30		8:30		8:30	
9:00		9:00		9:00		9:00	
9:30		9:30		9:30		9:30	
10:00		10:00		10:00		10:00	
10:30		10:30		10:30		10:30	
11:00		11:00		11:00		11:00	
	( )		( )		( )		( )

Week of:	Sunday		Monday		Tuesday	
This Week's Goal	S		S		S	
	A		A		A	
	V		V		V	
	E		E		E	
	R		R		R	
	S		S		S	
Intention for the Day	◆		◆		◆	
Grateful for …	◆		◆		◆	

There are only two ways to live your life. One is as though nothing is a miracle. The other is as though everything is a miracle.

—ALBERT EINSTEIN

TO-DO LIST
Highest Priority
Definite Priority
Lowest Priority
Habit to Work on This Week

Sunday	Monday	Tuesday
5:00	5:00	5:00
5:30	5:30	5:30
6:00	6:00	6:00
6:30	6:30	6:30
7:00	7:00	7:00
7:30	7:30	7:30
8:00	8:00	8:00
8:30	8:30	8:30
9:00	9:00	9:00
9:30	9:30	9:30
10:00	10:00	10:00
10:30	10:30	10:30
11:00	11:00	11:00
11:30	11:30	11:30
12:00	12:00	12:00
12:30	12:30	12:30
1:00	1:00	1:00
1:30	1:30	1:30
2:00	2:00	2:00
2:30	2:30	2:30
3:00	3:00	3:00
3:30	3:30	3:30
4:00	4:00	4:00
4:30	4:30	4:30
5:00	5:00	5:00
5:30	5:30	5:30
6:00	6:00	6:00
6:30	6:30	6:30
7:00	7:00	7:00
7:30	7:30	7:30
8:00	8:00	8:00
8:30	8:30	8:30
9:00	9:00	9:00
9:30	9:30	9:30
10:00	10:00	10:00
10:30	10:30	10:30
11:00	11:00	11:00

Ready for tomorrow?	( )	( )	( )
ALARM			
CLOTHES			
GLASS OF WATER			
SAVERS PREP			
BEDTIME AFFIRMATIONS			

Wednesday		Thursday		Friday		Saturday	
S		S		S		S	
A		A		A		A	
V		V		V		V	
E		E		E		E	
R		R		R		R	
S		S		S		S	
◆		◆		◆		◆	
◆		◆		◆		◆	
5:00		5:00		5:00		5:00	
5:30		5:30		5:30		5:30	
6:00		6:00		6:00		6:00	
6:30		6:30		6:30		6:30	
7:00		7:00		7:00		7:00	
7:30		7:30		7:30		7:30	
8:00		8:00		8:00		8:00	
8:30		8:30		8:30		8:30	
9:00		9:00		9:00		9:00	
9:30		9:30		9:30		9:30	
10:00		10:00		10:00		10:00	
10:30		10:30		10:30		10:30	
11:00		11:00		11:00		11:00	
11:30		11:30		11:30		11:30	
12:00		12:00		12:00		12:00	
12:30		12:30		12:30		12:30	
1:00		1:00		1:00		1:00	
1:30		1:30		1:30		1:30	
2:00		2:00		2:00		2:00	
2:30		2:30		2:30		2:30	
3:00		3:00		3:00		3:00	
3:30		3:30		3:30		3:30	
4:00		4:00		4:00		4:00	
4:30		4:30		4:30		4:30	
5:00		5:00		5:00		5:00	
5:30		5:30		5:30		5:30	
6:00		6:00		6:00		6:00	
6:30		6:30		6:30		6:30	
7:00		7:00		7:00		7:00	
7:30		7:30		7:30		7:30	
8:00		8:00		8:00		8:00	
8:30		8:30		8:30		8:30	
9:00		9:00		9:00		9:00	
9:30		9:30		9:30		9:30	
10:00		10:00		10:00		10:00	
10:30		10:30		10:30		10:30	
11:00		11:00		11:00		11:00	
( )		( )		( )		( )	

MONTHLY REFLECTION

. . . .

Write 5 things you accomplished this month:

1.

2.

3.

4.

5.

QUESTIONS

1) What did I learn about myself this month?

2) What tasks are left over from this month that are lingering and need to get done?

3. Did I take care of myself?

4) What could I have done differently this past month?

5) What areas can I (still) improve on?

6) What experiences can I treasure?

7) What challenged me and how did I overcome the challenge?

8) What specific habits and/or rituals could I develop this month to support my vision?

MONTH OF:	SUNDAY	MONDAY	TUESDAY
This Month's Goal			
Important Events or Reminders to Transfer to My Phone			
1.			
2.			
3.			
4.			
5.			
6.			
7.			
8.			
9.			
10.			

PROJECT NAME	TEAM PLAYERS	IMPORTANT DATES	DEADLINES
1.			
2.			
3.			
4.			

WEDNESDAY	THURSDAY	FRIDAY	SATURDAY

BRAINSTORM

Week of:	Sunday		Monday		Tuesday	
This Week's Goal	S		S		S	
	A		A		A	
	V		V		V	
	E		E		E	
	R		R		R	
	S		S		S	
Intention for the Day	◆		◆		◆	
Grateful for ...	◆		◆		◆	

	Sunday	Monday	Tuesday
An extraordinary life is all about daily, continuous improvements in the areas that matter most. —ROBIN SHARMA	5:00	5:00	5:00
	5:30	5:30	5:30
	6:00	6:00	6:00
	6:30	6:30	6:30
	7:00	7:00	7:00
	7:30	7:30	7:30
	8:00	8:00	8:00
	8:30	8:30	8:30
	9:00	9:00	9:00
	9:30	9:30	9:30
TO-DO LIST	10:00	10:00	10:00
Highest Priority	10:30	10:30	10:30
	11:00	11:00	11:00
	11:30	11:30	11:30
	12:00	12:00	12:00
	12:30	12:30	12:30
	1:00	1:00	1:00
Definite Priority	1:30	1:30	1:30
	2:00	2:00	2:00
	2:30	2:30	2:30
	3:00	3:00	3:00
	3:30	3:30	3:30
	4:00	4:00	4:00
Lowest Priority	4:30	4:30	4:30
	5:00	5:00	5:00
	5:30	5:30	5:30
	6:00	6:00	6:00
	6:30	6:30	6:30
	7:00	7:00	7:00
	7:30	7:30	7:30
Habit to Work on This Week	8:00	8:00	8:00
	8:30	8:30	8:30
	9:00	9:00	9:00
	9:30	9:30	9:30
	10:00	10:00	10:00
	10:30	10:30	10:30
	11:00	11:00	11:00

Ready for tomorrow?	( )	( )	( )
ALARM			
CLOTHES			
GLASS OF WATER			
SAVERS PREP			
BEDTIME AFFIRMATIONS			

Wednesday		Thursday		Friday		Saturday	
S		S		S		S	
A		A		A		A	
V		V		V		V	
E		E		E		E	
R		R		R		R	
S		S		S		S	
◆		◆		◆		◆	
◆		◆		◆		◆	
5:00		5:00		5:00		5:00	
5:30		5:30		5:30		5:30	
6:00		6:00		6:00		6:00	
6:30		6:30		6:30		6:30	
7:00		7:00		7:00		7:00	
7:30		7:30		7:30		7:30	
8:00		8:00		8:00		8:00	
8:30		8:30		8:30		8:30	
9:00		9:00		9:00		9:00	
9:30		9:30		9:30		9:30	
10:00		10:00		10:00		10:00	
10:30		10:30		10:30		10:30	
11:00		11:00		11:00		11:00	
11:30		11:30		11:30		11:30	
12:00		12:00		12:00		12:00	
12:30		12:30		12:30		12:30	
1:00		1:00		1:00		1:00	
1:30		1:30		1:30		1:30	
2:00		2:00		2:00		2:00	
2:30		2:30		2:30		2:30	
3:00		3:00		3:00		3:00	
3:30		3:30		3:30		3:30	
4:00		4:00		4:00		4:00	
4:30		4:30		4:30		4:30	
5:00		5:00		5:00		5:00	
5:30		5:30		5:30		5:30	
6:00		6:00		6:00		6:00	
6:30		6:30		6:30		6:30	
7:00		7:00		7:00		7:00	
7:30		7:30		7:30		7:30	
8:00		8:00		8:00		8:00	
8:30		8:30		8:30		8:30	
9:00		9:00		9:00		9:00	
9:30		9:30		9:30		9:30	
10:00		10:00		10:00		10:00	
10:30		10:30		10:30		10:30	
11:00		11:00		11:00		11:00	
	( )		( )		( )		( )

Week of:	Sunday		Monday		Tuesday	
This Week's Goal	S		S		S	
	A		A		A	
	V		V		V	
	E		E		E	
	R		R		R	
	S		S		S	
Intention for the Day	◆		◆		◆	
Grateful for ...	◆		◆		◆	

Whether you think you can or you think you can't, you're right.

—HENRY FORD

TO-DO LIST

Highest Priority

Definite Priority

Lowest Priority

Habit to Work on This Week

	Sunday	Monday	Tuesday
5:00		5:00	5:00
5:30		5:30	5:30
6:00		6:00	6:00
6:30		6:30	6:30
7:00		7:00	7:00
7:30		7:30	7:30
8:00		8:00	8:00
8:30		8:30	8:30
9:00		9:00	9:00
9:30		9:30	9:30
10:00		10:00	10:00
10:30		10:30	10:30
11:00		11:00	11:00
11:30		11:30	11:30
12:00		12:00	12:00
12:30		12:30	12:30
1:00		1:00	1:00
1:30		1:30	1:30
2:00		2:00	2:00
2:30		2:30	2:30
3:00		3:00	3:00
3:30		3:30	3:30
4:00		4:00	4:00
4:30		4:30	4:30
5:00		5:00	5:00
5:30		5:30	5:30
6:00		6:00	6:00
6:30		6:30	6:30
7:00		7:00	7:00
7:30		7:30	7:30
8:00		8:00	8:00
8:30		8:30	8:30
9:00		9:00	9:00
9:30		9:30	9:30
10:00		10:00	10:00
10:30		10:30	10:30
11:00		11:00	11:00

Ready for tomorrow?	( )	( )	( )
ALARM			
CLOTHES			
GLASS OF WATER			
SAVERS PREP			
BEDTIME AFFIRMATIONS			

Wednesday		Thursday		Friday		Saturday	
S		S		S		S	
A		A		A		A	
V		V		V		V	
E		E		E		E	
R		R		R		R	
S		S		S		S	
◆		◆		◆		◆	
◆		◆		◆		◆	
5:00		5:00		5:00		5:00	
5:30		5:30		5:30		5:30	
6:00		6:00		6:00		6:00	
6:30		6:30		6:30		6:30	
7:00		7:00		7:00		7:00	
7:30		7:30		7:30		7:30	
8:00		8:00		8:00		8:00	
8:30		8:30		8:30		8:30	
9:00		9:00		9:00		9:00	
9:30		9:30		9:30		9:30	
10:00		10:00		10:00		10:00	
10:30		10:30		10:30		10:30	
11:00		11:00		11:00		11:00	
11:30		11:30		11:30		11:30	
12:00		12:00		12:00		12:00	
12:30		12:30		12:30		12:30	
1:00		1:00		1:00		1:00	
1:30		1:30		1:30		1:30	
2:00		2:00		2:00		2:00	
2:30		2:30		2:30		2:30	
3:00		3:00		3:00		3:00	
3:30		3:30		3:30		3:30	
4:00		4:00		4:00		4:00	
4:30		4:30		4:30		4:30	
5:00		5:00		5:00		5:00	
5:30		5:30		5:30		5:30	
6:00		6:00		6:00		6:00	
6:30		6:30		6:30		6:30	
7:00		7:00		7:00		7:00	
7:30		7:30		7:30		7:30	
8:00		8:00		8:00		8:00	
8:30		8:30		8:30		8:30	
9:00		9:00		9:00		9:00	
9:30		9:30		9:30		9:30	
10:00		10:00		10:00		10:00	
10:30		10:30		10:30		10:30	
11:00		11:00		11:00		11:00	
	( )		( )		( )		( )

Week of:	Sunday		Monday		Tuesday	
This Week's Goal	S		S		S	
	A		A		A	
	V		V		V	
	E		E		E	
	R		R		R	
	S		S		S	
Intention for the Day	◆		◆		◆	
Grateful for ...	◆		◆		◆	

	Sunday	Monday	Tuesday
You miss 100% of the shots you don't take. —WAYNE GRETZKY	5:00	5:00	5:00
	5:30	5:30	5:30
	6:00	6:00	6:00
	6:30	6:30	6:30
	7:00	7:00	7:00
	7:30	7:30	7:30
	8:00	8:00	8:00
	8:30	8:30	8:30
	9:00	9:00	9:00
	9:30	9:30	9:30
TO-DO LIST	10:00	10:00	10:00
Highest Priority	10:30	10:30	10:30
	11:00	11:00	11:00
	11:30	11:30	11:30
	12:00	12:00	12:00
	12:30	12:30	12:30
	1:00	1:00	1:00
Definite Priority	1:30	1:30	1:30
	2:00	2:00	2:00
	2:30	2:30	2:30
	3:00	3:00	3:00
	3:30	3:30	3:30
	4:00	4:00	4:00
Lowest Priority	4:30	4:30	4:30
	5:00	5:00	5:00
	5:30	5:30	5:30
	6:00	6:00	6:00
	6:30	6:30	6:30
	7:00	7:00	7:00
	7:30	7:30	7:30
Habit to Work on This Week	8:00	8:00	8:00
	8:30	8:30	8:30
	9:00	9:00	9:00
	9:30	9:30	9:30
	10:00	10:00	10:00
	10:30	10:30	10:30
	11:00	11:00	11:00

Ready for tomorrow?	( )	( )	( )
ALARM			
CLOTHES			
GLASS OF WATER			
SAVERS PREP			
BEDTIME AFFIRMATIONS			

Wednesday	Thursday	Friday	Saturday
S	S	S	S
A	A	A	A
V	V	V	V
E	E	E	E
R	R	R	R
S	S	S	S

◆	◆	◆	◆
◆	◆	◆	◆

Wednesday		Thursday		Friday		Saturday	
5:00		5:00		5:00		5:00	
5:30		5:30		5:30		5:30	
6:00		6:00		6:00		6:00	
6:30		6:30		6:30		6:30	
7:00		7:00		7:00		7:00	
7:30		7:30		7:30		7:30	
8:00		8:00		8:00		8:00	
8:30		8:30		8:30		8:30	
9:00		9:00		9:00		9:00	
9:30		9:30		9:30		9:30	
10:00		10:00		10:00		10:00	
10:30		10:30		10:30		10:30	
11:00		11:00		11:00		11:00	
11:30		11:30		11:30		11:30	
12:00		12:00		12:00		12:00	
12:30		12:30		12:30		12:30	
1:00		1:00		1:00		1:00	
1:30		1:30		1:30		1:30	
2:00		2:00		2:00		2:00	
2:30		2:30		2:30		2:30	
3:00		3:00		3:00		3:00	
3:30		3:30		3:30		3:30	
4:00		4:00		4:00		4:00	
4:30		4:30		4:30		4:30	
5:00		5:00		5:00		5:00	
5:30		5:30		5:30		5:30	
6:00		6:00		6:00		6:00	
6:30		6:30		6:30		6:30	
7:00		7:00		7:00		7:00	
7:30		7:30		7:30		7:30	
8:00		8:00		8:00		8:00	
8:30		8:30		8:30		8:30	
9:00		9:00		9:00		9:00	
9:30		9:30		9:30		9:30	
10:00		10:00		10:00		10:00	
10:30		10:30		10:30		10:30	
11:00		11:00		11:00		11:00	
( )		( )		( )		( )	

Week of:	Sunday		Monday		Tuesday	
This Week's Goal	S		S		S	
	A		A		A	
	V		V		V	
	E		E		E	
	R		R		R	
	S		S		S	
Intention for the Day	◆		◆		◆	
Grateful for ...	◆		◆		◆	

	Sunday	Monday	Tuesday
Success is going from failure to failure without losing your enthusiasm. —WINSTON CHURCHILL	5:00	5:00	5:00
	5:30	5:30	5:30
	6:00	6:00	6:00
	6:30	6:30	6:30
	7:00	7:00	7:00
	7:30	7:30	7:30
	8:00	8:00	8:00
	8:30	8:30	8:30
	9:00	9:00	9:00
	9:30	9:30	9:30
TO-DO LIST	10:00	10:00	10:00
Highest Priority	10:30	10:30	10:30
	11:00	11:00	11:00
	11:30	11:30	11:30
	12:00	12:00	12:00
	12:30	12:30	12:30
	1:00	1:00	1:00
Definite Priority	1:30	1:30	1:30
	2:00	2:00	2:00
	2:30	2:30	2:30
	3:00	3:00	3:00
	3:30	3:30	3:30
	4:00	4:00	4:00
Lowest Priority	4:30	4:30	4:30
	5:00	5:00	5:00
	5:30	5:30	5:30
	6:00	6:00	6:00
	6:30	6:30	6:30
	7:00	7:00	7:00
	7:30	7:30	7:30
Habit to Work on This Week	8:00	8:00	8:00
	8:30	8:30	8:30
	9:00	9:00	9:00
	9:30	9:30	9:30
	10:00	10:00	10:00
	10:30	10:30	10:30
	11:00	11:00	11:00

Ready for tomorrow?	( )	( )	( )
ALARM			
CLOTHES			
GLASS OF WATER			
SAVERS PREP			
BEDTIME AFFIRMATIONS			

Wednesday		Thursday		Friday		Saturday	
S		S		S		S	
A		A		A		A	
V		V		V		V	
E		E		E		E	
R		R		R		R	
S		S		S		S	
◆		◆		◆		◆	
◆		◆		◆		◆	
5:00		5:00		5:00		5:00	
5:30		5:30		5:30		5:30	
6:00		6:00		6:00		6:00	
6:30		6:30		6:30		6:30	
7:00		7:00		7:00		7:00	
7:30		7:30		7:30		7:30	
8:00		8:00		8:00		8:00	
8:30		8:30		8:30		8:30	
9:00		9:00		9:00		9:00	
9:30		9:30		9:30		9:30	
10:00		10:00		10:00		10:00	
10:30		10:30		10:30		10:30	
11:00		11:00		11:00		11:00	
11:30		11:30		11:30		11:30	
12:00		12:00		12:00		12:00	
12:30		12:30		12:30		12:30	
1:00		1:00		1:00		1:00	
1:30		1:30		1:30		1:30	
2:00		2:00		2:00		2:00	
2:30		2:30		2:30		2:30	
3:00		3:00		3:00		3:00	
3:30		3:30		3:30		3:30	
4:00		4:00		4:00		4:00	
4:30		4:30		4:30		4:30	
5:00		5:00		5:00		5:00	
5:30		5:30		5:30		5:30	
6:00		6:00		6:00		6:00	
6:30		6:30		6:30		6:30	
7:00		7:00		7:00		7:00	
7:30		7:30		7:30		7:30	
8:00		8:00		8:00		8:00	
8:30		8:30		8:30		8:30	
9:00		9:00		9:00		9:00	
9:30		9:30		9:30		9:30	
10:00		10:00		10:00		10:00	
10:30		10:30		10:30		10:30	
11:00		11:00		11:00		11:00	
( )		( )		( )		( )	

Week of:	Sunday	Monday	Tuesday
This Week's Goal	S	S	S
	A	A	A
	V	V	V
	E	E	E
	R	R	R
	S	S	S
Intention for the Day	◆	◆	◆
Grateful for ...	◆	◆	◆

	Sunday	Monday	Tuesday
Whatever you can do, or dream you can, begin it. Boldness has genius, power and magic in it. **–JOHANN WOLFGANG VON GOETHE**	5:00	5:00	5:00
	5:30	5:30	5:30
	6:00	6:00	6:00
	6:30	6:30	6:30
	7:00	7:00	7:00
	7:30	7:30	7:30
	8:00	8:00	8:00
	8:30	8:30	8:30
	9:00	9:00	9:00
	9:30	9:30	9:30
TO-DO LIST	10:00	10:00	10:00
Highest Priority	10:30	10:30	10:30
	11:00	11:00	11:00
	11:30	11:30	11:30
	12:00	12:00	12:00
	12:30	12:30	12:30
	1:00	1:00	1:00
Definite Priority	1:30	1:30	1:30
	2:00	2:00	2:00
	2:30	2:30	2:30
	3:00	3:00	3:00
	3:30	3:30	3:30
	4:00	4:00	4:00
Lowest Priority	4:30	4:30	4:30
	5:00	5:00	5:00
	5:30	5:30	5:30
	6:00	6:00	6:00
	6:30	6:30	6:30
	7:00	7:00	7:00
	7:30	7:30	7:30
Habit to Work on This Week	8:00	8:00	8:00
	8:30	8:30	8:30
	9:00	9:00	9:00
	9:30	9:30	9:30
	10:00	10:00	10:00
	10:30	10:30	10:30
	11:00	11:00	11:00

Ready for tomorrow?	( )	( )	( )
ALARM			
CLOTHES			
GLASS OF WATER			
SAVERS PREP			
BEDTIME AFFIRMATIONS			

Wednesday		Thursday		Friday		Saturday	
S		S		S		S	
A		A		A		A	
V		V		V		V	
E		E		E		E	
R		R		R		R	
S		S		S		S	
◆		◆		◆		◆	
◆		◆		◆		◆	
5:00		5:00		5:00		5:00	
5:30		5:30		5:30		5:30	
6:00		6:00		6:00		6:00	
6:30		6:30		6:30		6:30	
7:00		7:00		7:00		7:00	
7:30		7:30		7:30		7:30	
8:00		8:00		8:00		8:00	
8:30		8:30		8:30		8:30	
9:00		9:00		9:00		9:00	
9:30		9:30		9:30		9:30	
10:00		10:00		10:00		10:00	
10:30		10:30		10:30		10:30	
11:00		11:00		11:00		11:00	
11:30		11:30		11:30		11:30	
12:00		12:00		12:00		12:00	
12:30		12:30		12:30		12:30	
1:00		1:00		1:00		1:00	
1:30		1:30		1:30		1:30	
2:00		2:00		2:00		2:00	
2:30		2:30		2:30		2:30	
3:00		3:00		3:00		3:00	
3:30		3:30		3:30		3:30	
4:00		4:00		4:00		4:00	
4:30		4:30		4:30		4:30	
5:00		5:00		5:00		5:00	
5:30		5:30		5:30		5:30	
6:00		6:00		6:00		6:00	
6:30		6:30		6:30		6:30	
7:00		7:00		7:00		7:00	
7:30		7:30		7:30		7:30	
8:00		8:00		8:00		8:00	
8:30		8:30		8:30		8:30	
9:00		9:00		9:00		9:00	
9:30		9:30		9:30		9:30	
10:00		10:00		10:00		10:00	
10:30		10:30		10:30		10:30	
11:00		11:00		11:00		11:00	
	( )		( )		( )		( )

MONTHLY REFLECTION

....

1.

2.

3.

4.

5.

QUESTIONS

1) What did I learn about myself this month?

2) What tasks are left over from this month that are lingering and need to get done?

3. Did I take care of myself?

4) What could I have done differently this past month?

5) What areas can I (still) improve on?

6) What experiences can I treasure?

7) What challenged me and how did I overcome the challenge?

8) What specific habits and/or rituals could I develop this month to support my vision?

MONTH OF:	SUNDAY	MONDAY	TUESDAY
This Month's Goal			
Important Events or Reminders to Transfer to My Phone			
1.			
2.			
3.			
4.			
5.			
6.			
7.			
8.			
9.			
10.			

PROJECT NAME	TEAM PLAYERS	IMPORTANT DATES	DEADLINES
1.			
2.			
3.			
4.			

WEDNESDAY	THURSDAY	FRIDAY	SATURDAY

BRAINSTORM

Week of:	Sunday		Monday		Tuesday	
This Week's Goal	S		S		S	
	A		A		A	
	V		V		V	
	E		E		E	
	R		R		R	
	S		S		S	
Intention for the Day	◆		◆		◆	
Grateful for ...	◆		◆		◆	

Where you are is a result of who you were, where you go depends entirely on the person you choose to be from this moment forward.

—HAL ELROD

TO-DO LIST	Sunday	Monday	Tuesday
Highest Priority	5:00	5:00	5:00
	5:30	5:30	5:30
	6:00	6:00	6:00
	6:30	6:30	6:30
	7:00	7:00	7:00
	7:30	7:30	7:30
	8:00	8:00	8:00
	8:30	8:30	8:30
	9:00	9:00	9:00
	9:30	9:30	9:30
	10:00	10:00	10:00
	10:30	10:30	10:30
	11:00	11:00	11:00
	11:30	11:30	11:30
	12:00	12:00	12:00
	12:30	12:30	12:30
	1:00	1:00	1:00
Definite Priority	1:30	1:30	1:30
	2:00	2:00	2:00
	2:30	2:30	2:30
	3:00	3:00	3:00
	3:30	3:30	3:30
	4:00	4:00	4:00
Lowest Priority	4:30	4:30	4:30
	5:00	5:00	5:00
	5:30	5:30	5:30
	6:00	6:00	6:00
	6:30	6:30	6:30
	7:00	7:00	7:00
	7:30	7:30	7:30
Habit to Work on This Week	8:00	8:00	8:00
	8:30	8:30	8:30
	9:00	9:00	9:00
	9:30	9:30	9:30
	10:00	10:00	10:00
	10:30	10:30	10:30
	11:00	11:00	11:00

Ready for tomorrow?	( )	( )	( )
ALARM			
CLOTHES			
GLASS OF WATER			
SAVERS PREP			
BEDTIME AFFIRMATIONS			

Wednesday		Thursday		Friday		Saturday	
S		S		S		S	
A		A		A		A	
V		V		V		V	
E		E		E		E	
R		R		R		R	
S		S		S		S	
◆		◆		◆		◆	
◆		◆		◆		◆	
5:00		5:00		5:00		5:00	
5:30		5:30		5:30		5:30	
6:00		6:00		6:00		6:00	
6:30		6:30		6:30		6:30	
7:00		7:00		7:00		7:00	
7:30		7:30		7:30		7:30	
8:00		8:00		8:00		8:00	
8:30		8:30		8:30		8:30	
9:00		9:00		9:00		9:00	
9:30		9:30		9:30		9:30	
10:00		10:00		10:00		10:00	
10:30		10:30		10:30		10:30	
11:00		11:00		11:00		11:00	
11:30		11:30		11:30		11:30	
12:00		12:00		12:00		12:00	
12:30		12:30		12:30		12:30	
1:00		1:00		1:00		1:00	
1:30		1:30		1:30		1:30	
2:00		2:00		2:00		2:00	
2:30		2:30		2:30		2:30	
3:00		3:00		3:00		3:00	
3:30		3:30		3:30		3:30	
4:00		4:00		4:00		4:00	
4:30		4:30		4:30		4:30	
5:00		5:00		5:00		5:00	
5:30		5:30		5:30		5:30	
6:00		6:00		6:00		6:00	
6:30		6:30		6:30		6:30	
7:00		7:00		7:00		7:00	
7:30		7:30		7:30		7:30	
8:00		8:00		8:00		8:00	
8:30		8:30		8:30		8:30	
9:00		9:00		9:00		9:00	
9:30		9:30		9:30		9:30	
10:00		10:00		10:00		10:00	
10:30		10:30		10:30		10:30	
11:00		11:00		11:00		11:00	
	( )		( )		( )		( )

Week of:	Sunday	Monday	Tuesday
This Week's Goal	S	S	S
	A	A	A
	V	V	V
	E	E	E
	R	R	R
	S	S	S
Intention for the Day	◆	◆	◆
Grateful for ...	◆	◆	◆

The successful warrior is the average man, with laser-like focus.

—**BRUCE LEE**

TO-DO LIST			
Highest Priority			
Definite Priority			
Lowest Priority			
Habit to Work on This Week			

	Sunday	Monday	Tuesday
5:00		5:00	5:00
5:30		5:30	5:30
6:00		6:00	6:00
6:30		6:30	6:30
7:00		7:00	7:00
7:30		7:30	7:30
8:00		8:00	8:00
8:30		8:30	8:30
9:00		9:00	9:00
9:30		9:30	9:30
10:00		10:00	10:00
10:30		10:30	10:30
11:00		11:00	11:00
11:30		11:30	11:30
12:00		12:00	12:00
12:30		12:30	12:30
1:00		1:00	1:00
1:30		1:30	1:30
2:00		2:00	2:00
2:30		2:30	2:30
3:00		3:00	3:00
3:30		3:30	3:30
4:00		4:00	4:00
4:30		4:30	4:30
5:00		5:00	5:00
5:30		5:30	5:30
6:00		6:00	6:00
6:30		6:30	6:30
7:00		7:00	7:00
7:30		7:30	7:30
8:00		8:00	8:00
8:30		8:30	8:30
9:00		9:00	9:00
9:30		9:30	9:30
10:00		10:00	10:00
10:30		10:30	10:30
11:00		11:00	11:00

Ready for tomorrow?	( )	( )	( )
ALARM			
CLOTHES			
GLASS OF WATER			
SAVERS PREP			
BEDTIME AFFIRMATIONS			

Wednesday	Thursday	Friday	Saturday
S	S	S	S
A	A	A	A
V	V	V	V
E	E	E	E
R	R	R	R
S	S	S	S

◆	◆	◆	◆
◆	◆	◆	◆

Wednesday		Thursday		Friday		Saturday	
5:00		5:00		5:00		5:00	
5:30		5:30		5:30		5:30	
6:00		6:00		6:00		6:00	
6:30		6:30		6:30		6:30	
7:00		7:00		7:00		7:00	
7:30		7:30		7:30		7:30	
8:00		8:00		8:00		8:00	
8:30		8:30		8:30		8:30	
9:00		9:00		9:00		9:00	
9:30		9:30		9:30		9:30	
10:00		10:00		10:00		10:00	
10:30		10:30		10:30		10:30	
11:00		11:00		11:00		11:00	
11:30		11:30		11:30		11:30	
12:00		12:00		12:00		12:00	
12:30		12:30		12:30		12:30	
1:00		1:00		1:00		1:00	
1:30		1:30		1:30		1:30	
2:00		2:00		2:00		2:00	
2:30		2:30		2:30		2:30	
3:00		3:00		3:00		3:00	
3:30		3:30		3:30		3:30	
4:00		4:00		4:00		4:00	
4:30		4:30		4:30		4:30	
5:00		5:00		5:00		5:00	
5:30		5:30		5:30		5:30	
6:00		6:00		6:00		6:00	
6:30		6:30		6:30		6:30	
7:00		7:00		7:00		7:00	
7:30		7:30		7:30		7:30	
8:00		8:00		8:00		8:00	
8:30		8:30		8:30		8:30	
9:00		9:00		9:00		9:00	
9:30		9:30		9:30		9:30	
10:00		10:00		10:00		10:00	
10:30		10:30		10:30		10:30	
11:00		11:00		11:00		11:00	
	( )		( )		( )		( )

Week of:	Sunday	Monday	Tuesday
This Week's Goal	S	S	S
	A	A	A
	V	V	V
	E	E	E
	R	R	R
	S	S	S
Intention for the Day	◆	◆	◆
Grateful for ...	◆	◆	◆

	Sunday	Monday	Tuesday
We make a living by what we get. We make a life by what we give. —WINSTON CHURCHILL	5:00	5:00	5:00
	5:30	5:30	5:30
	6:00	6:00	6:00
	6:30	6:30	6:30
	7:00	7:00	7:00
	7:30	7:30	7:30
	8:00	8:00	8:00
	8:30	8:30	8:30
	9:00	9:00	9:00
	9:30	9:30	9:30
TO-DO LIST	10:00	10:00	10:00
Highest Priority	10:30	10:30	10:30
	11:00	11:00	11:00
	11:30	11:30	11:30
	12:00	12:00	12:00
	12:30	12:30	12:30
	1:00	1:00	1:00
Definite Priority	1:30	1:30	1:30
	2:00	2:00	2:00
	2:30	2:30	2:30
	3:00	3:00	3:00
	3:30	3:30	3:30
	4:00	4:00	4:00
Lowest Priority	4:30	4:30	4:30
	5:00	5:00	5:00
	5:30	5:30	5:30
	6:00	6:00	6:00
	6:30	6:30	6:30
	7:00	7:00	7:00
	7:30	7:30	7:30
Habit to Work on This Week	8:00	8:00	8:00
	8:30	8:30	8:30
	9:00	9:00	9:00
	9:30	9:30	9:30
	10:00	10:00	10:00
	10:30	10:30	10:30
	11:00	11:00	11:00

Ready for tomorrow?	( )	( )	( )
ALARM			
CLOTHES			
GLASS OF WATER			
SAVERS PREP			
BEDTIME AFFIRMATIONS			

Wednesday	Thursday	Friday	Saturday
S	S	S	S
A	A	A	A
V	V	V	V
E	E	E	E
R	R	R	R
S	S	S	S

◆	◆	◆	◆
◆	◆	◆	◆

Wednesday	Thursday	Friday	Saturday
5:00	5:00	5:00	5:00
5:30	5:30	5:30	5:30
6:00	6:00	6:00	6:00
6:30	6:30	6:30	6:30
7:00	7:00	7:00	7:00
7:30	7:30	7:30	7:30
8:00	8:00	8:00	8:00
8:30	8:30	8:30	8:30
9:00	9:00	9:00	9:00
9:30	9:30	9:30	9:30
10:00	10:00	10:00	10:00
10:30	10:30	10:30	10:30
11:00	11:00	11:00	11:00
11:30	11:30	11:30	11:30
12:00	12:00	12:00	12:00
12:30	12:30	12:30	12:30
1:00	1:00	1:00	1:00
1:30	1:30	1:30	1:30
2:00	2:00	2:00	2:00
2:30	2:30	2:30	2:30
3:00	3:00	3:00	3:00
3:30	3:30	3:30	3:30
4:00	4:00	4:00	4:00
4:30	4:30	4:30	4:30
5:00	5:00	5:00	5:00
5:30	5:30	5:30	5:30
6:00	6:00	6:00	6:00
6:30	6:30	6:30	6:30
7:00	7:00	7:00	7:00
7:30	7:30	7:30	7:30
8:00	8:00	8:00	8:00
8:30	8:30	8:30	8:30
9:00	9:00	9:00	9:00
9:30	9:30	9:30	9:30
10:00	10:00	10:00	10:00
10:30	10:30	10:30	10:30
11:00	11:00	11:00	11:00

( )	( )	( )	( )

Week of:	Sunday	Monday	Tuesday
This Week's Goal	S	S	S
	A	A	A
	V	V	V
	E	E	E
	R	R	R
	S	S	S
Intention for the Day	◆	◆	◆
Grateful for ...	◆	◆	◆

Dream Big. Work Hard.
Create Value.

— **JEFF HOFFMAN**

	Sunday	Monday	Tuesday
TO-DO LIST	5:00	5:00	5:00
Highest Priority	5:30	5:30	5:30
	6:00	6:00	6:00
	6:30	6:30	6:30
	7:00	7:00	7:00
	7:30	7:30	7:30
	8:00	8:00	8:00
	8:30	8:30	8:30
	9:00	9:00	9:00
	9:30	9:30	9:30
	10:00	10:00	10:00
	10:30	10:30	10:30
	11:00	11:00	11:00
	11:30	11:30	11:30
	12:00	12:00	12:00
	12:30	12:30	12:30
	1:00	1:00	1:00
Definite Priority	1:30	1:30	1:30
	2:00	2:00	2:00
	2:30	2:30	2:30
	3:00	3:00	3:00
	3:30	3:30	3:30
	4:00	4:00	4:00
Lowest Priority	4:30	4:30	4:30
	5:00	5:00	5:00
	5:30	5:30	5:30
	6:00	6:00	6:00
	6:30	6:30	6:30
	7:00	7:00	7:00
	7:30	7:30	7:30
Habit to Work on This Week	8:00	8:00	8:00
	8:30	8:30	8:30
	9:00	9:00	9:00
	9:30	9:30	9:30
	10:00	10:00	10:00
	10:30	10:30	10:30
	11:00	11:00	11:00

Ready for tomorrow?	( )	( )	( )
ALARM			
CLOTHES			
GLASS OF WATER			
SAVERS PREP			
BEDTIME AFFIRMATIONS			

Wednesday		Thursday		Friday		Saturday	
S		S		S		S	
A		A		A		A	
V		V		V		V	
E		E		E		E	
R		R		R		R	
S		S		S		S	
◆		◆		◆		◆	
◆		◆		◆		◆	
5:00		5:00		5:00		5:00	
5:30		5:30		5:30		5:30	
6:00		6:00		6:00		6:00	
6:30		6:30		6:30		6:30	
7:00		7:00		7:00		7:00	
7:30		7:30		7:30		7:30	
8:00		8:00		8:00		8:00	
8:30		8:30		8:30		8:30	
9:00		9:00		9:00		9:00	
9:30		9:30		9:30		9:30	
10:00		10:00		10:00		10:00	
10:30		10:30		10:30		10:30	
11:00		11:00		11:00		11:00	
11:30		11:30		11:30		11:30	
12:00		12:00		12:00		12:00	
12:30		12:30		12:30		12:30	
1:00		1:00		1:00		1:00	
1:30		1:30		1:30		1:30	
2:00		2:00		2:00		2:00	
2:30		2:30		2:30		2:30	
3:00		3:00		3:00		3:00	
3:30		3:30		3:30		3:30	
4:00		4:00		4:00		4:00	
4:30		4:30		4:30		4:30	
5:00		5:00		5:00		5:00	
5:30		5:30		5:30		5:30	
6:00		6:00		6:00		6:00	
6:30		6:30		6:30		6:30	
7:00		7:00		7:00		7:00	
7:30		7:30		7:30		7:30	
8:00		8:00		8:00		8:00	
8:30		8:30		8:30		8:30	
9:00		9:00		9:00		9:00	
9:30		9:30		9:30		9:30	
10:00		10:00		10:00		10:00	
10:30		10:30		10:30		10:30	
11:00		11:00		11:00		11:00	
	( )		( )		( )		( )

Week of:	Sunday	Monday	Tuesday
This Week's Goal	S	S	S
	A	A	A
	V	V	V
	E	E	E
	R	R	R
	S	S	S
Intention for the Day	◆	◆	◆
Grateful for ...	◆	◆	◆

Why not go out on a limb? That's where the fruit it is.

—MARK TWAIN

TO-DO LIST	Sunday	Monday	Tuesday
Highest Priority	5:00	5:00	5:00
	5:30	5:30	5:30
	6:00	6:00	6:00
	6:30	6:30	6:30
	7:00	7:00	7:00
	7:30	7:30	7:30
	8:00	8:00	8:00
	8:30	8:30	8:30
	9:00	9:00	9:00
	9:30	9:30	9:30
	10:00	10:00	10:00
	10:30	10:30	10:30
	11:00	11:00	11:00
	11:30	11:30	11:30
	12:00	12:00	12:00
	12:30	12:30	12:30
	1:00	1:00	1:00
Definite Priority	1:30	1:30	1:30
	2:00	2:00	2:00
	2:30	2:30	2:30
	3:00	3:00	3:00
	3:30	3:30	3:30
	4:00	4:00	4:00
	4:30	4:30	4:30
Lowest Priority	5:00	5:00	5:00
	5:30	5:30	5:30
	6:00	6:00	6:00
	6:30	6:30	6:30
	7:00	7:00	7:00
	7:30	7:30	7:30
Habit to Work on This Week	8:00	8:00	8:00
	8:30	8:30	8:30
	9:00	9:00	9:00
	9:30	9:30	9:30
	10:00	10:00	10:00
	10:30	10:30	10:30
	11:00	11:00	11:00

Ready for tomorrow?	( )	( )	( )
ALARM			
CLOTHES			
GLASS OF WATER			
SAVERS PREP			
BEDTIME AFFIRMATIONS			

Wednesday		Thursday		Friday		Saturday	
S		S		S		S	
A		A		A		A	
V		V		V		V	
E		E		E		E	
R		R		R		R	
S		S		S		S	
◆		◆		◆		◆	
◆		◆		◆		◆	
5:00		5:00		5:00		5:00	
5:30		5:30		5:30		5:30	
6:00		6:00		6:00		6:00	
6:30		6:30		6:30		6:30	
7:00		7:00		7:00		7:00	
7:30		7:30		7:30		7:30	
8:00		8:00		8:00		8:00	
8:30		8:30		8:30		8:30	
9:00		9:00		9:00		9:00	
9:30		9:30		9:30		9:30	
10:00		10:00		10:00		10:00	
10:30		10:30		10:30		10:30	
11:00		11:00		11:00		11:00	
11:30		11:30		11:30		11:30	
12:00		12:00		12:00		12:00	
12:30		12:30		12:30		12:30	
1:00		1:00		1:00		1:00	
1:30		1:30		1:30		1:30	
2:00		2:00		2:00		2:00	
2:30		2:30		2:30		2:30	
3:00		3:00		3:00		3:00	
3:30		3:30		3:30		3:30	
4:00		4:00		4:00		4:00	
4:30		4:30		4:30		4:30	
5:00		5:00		5:00		5:00	
5:30		5:30		5:30		5:30	
6:00		6:00		6:00		6:00	
6:30		6:30		6:30		6:30	
7:00		7:00		7:00		7:00	
7:30		7:30		7:30		7:30	
8:00		8:00		8:00		8:00	
8:30		8:30		8:30		8:30	
9:00		9:00		9:00		9:00	
9:30		9:30		9:30		9:30	
10:00		10:00		10:00		10:00	
10:30		10:30		10:30		10:30	
11:00		11:00		11:00		11:00	
	( )		( )		( )		( )

MONTHLY REFLECTION

· ·

Write 5 things you accomplished this month:

1.

2.

3.

4.

5.

QUESTIONS

1) What did I learn about myself this month?

2) What tasks are left over from this month that are lingering and need to get done?

3. Did I take care of myself?

4) What could I have done differently this past month?

5) What areas can I (still) improve on?

6) What experiences can I treasure?

7) What challenged me and how did I overcome the challenge?

8) What specific habits and/or rituals could I develop this month to support my vision?

MONTH OF:	SUNDAY	MONDAY	TUESDAY
This Month's Goal			
Important Events or Reminders to Transfer to My Phone			
1.			
2.			
3.			
4.			
5.			
6.			
7.			
8.			
9.			
10.			

PROJECT NAME	TEAM PLAYERS	IMPORTANT DATES	DEADLINES
1.			
2.			
3.			
4.			

WEDNESDAY	THURSDAY	FRIDAY	SATURDAY

BRAINSTORM

Week of:	Sunday	Monday	Tuesday
This Week's Goal	S	S	S
	A	A	A
	V	V	V
	E	E	E
	R	R	R
	S	S	S
Intention for the Day	◆	◆	◆
Grateful for ...	◆	◆	◆

	Sunday	Monday	Tuesday
Whatever the mind of man can conceive and believe, it can achieve. —NAPOLEON HILL	5:00	5:00	5:00
	5:30	5:30	5:30
	6:00	6:00	6:00
	6:30	6:30	6:30
	7:00	7:00	7:00
	7:30	7:30	7:30
	8:00	8:00	8:00
	8:30	8:30	8:30
	9:00	9:00	9:00
	9:30	9:30	9:30
TO-DO LIST	10:00	10:00	10:00
Highest Priority	10:30	10:30	10:30
	11:00	11:00	11:00
	11:30	11:30	11:30
	12:00	12:00	12:00
	12:30	12:30	12:30
	1:00	1:00	1:00
Definite Priority	1:30	1:30	1:30
	2:00	2:00	2:00
	2:30	2:30	2:30
	3:00	3:00	3:00
	3:30	3:30	3:30
	4:00	4:00	4:00
Lowest Priority	4:30	4:30	4:30
	5:00	5:00	5:00
	5:30	5:30	5:30
	6:00	6:00	6:00
	6:30	6:30	6:30
	7:00	7:00	7:00
	7:30	7:30	7:30
Habit to Work on This Week	8:00	8:00	8:00
	8:30	8:30	8:30
	9:00	9:00	9:00
	9:30	9:30	9:30
	10:00	10:00	10:00
	10:30	10:30	10:30
	11:00	11:00	11:00
Ready for tomorrow?	( )	( )	( )
ALARM			
CLOTHES			
GLASS OF WATER			
SAVERS PREP			
BEDTIME AFFIRMATIONS			

Wednesday	Thursday	Friday	Saturday
S	S	S	S
A	A	A	A
V	V	V	V
E	E	E	E
R	R	R	R
S	S	S	S

◆	◆	◆	◆
◆	◆	◆	◆

Time	Wednesday	Time	Thursday	Time	Friday	Time	Saturday
5:00		5:00		5:00		5:00	
5:30		5:30		5:30		5:30	
6:00		6:00		6:00		6:00	
6:30		6:30		6:30		6:30	
7:00		7:00		7:00		7:00	
7:30		7:30		7:30		7:30	
8:00		8:00		8:00		8:00	
8:30		8:30		8:30		8:30	
9:00		9:00		9:00		9:00	
9:30		9:30		9:30		9:30	
10:00		10:00		10:00		10:00	
10:30		10:30		10:30		10:30	
11:00		11:00		11:00		11:00	
11:30		11:30		11:30		11:30	
12:00		12:00		12:00		12:00	
12:30		12:30		12:30		12:30	
1:00		1:00		1:00		1:00	
1:30		1:30		1:30		1:30	
2:00		2:00		2:00		2:00	
2:30		2:30		2:30		2:30	
3:00		3:00		3:00		3:00	
3:30		3:30		3:30		3:30	
4:00		4:00		4:00		4:00	
4:30		4:30		4:30		4:30	
5:00		5:00		5:00		5:00	
5:30		5:30		5:30		5:30	
6:00		6:00		6:00		6:00	
6:30		6:30		6:30		6:30	
7:00		7:00		7:00		7:00	
7:30		7:30		7:30		7:30	
8:00		8:00		8:00		8:00	
8:30		8:30		8:30		8:30	
9:00		9:00		9:00		9:00	
9:30		9:30		9:30		9:30	
10:00		10:00		10:00		10:00	
10:30		10:30		10:30		10:30	
11:00		11:00		11:00		11:00	

( )	( )	( )	( )

Week of:	Sunday	Monday	Tuesday
This Week's Goal	S	S	S
	A	A	A
	V	V	V
	E	E	E
	R	R	R
	S	S	S
Intention for the Day	◆	◆	◆
Grateful for ...	◆	◆	◆

Strive not to be a success, but rather to be of value.

—ALBERT EINSTEIN

TO-DO LIST

Highest Priority

Definite Priority

Lowest Priority

Habit to Work on This Week

	Sunday	Monday	Tuesday
5:00		5:00		5:00	
5:30		5:30		5:30	
6:00		6:00		6:00	
6:30		6:30		6:30	
7:00		7:00		7:00	
7:30		7:30		7:30	
8:00		8:00		8:00	
8:30		8:30		8:30	
9:00		9:00		9:00	
9:30		9:30		9:30	
10:00		10:00		10:00	
10:30		10:30		10:30	
11:00		11:00		11:00	
11:30		11:30		11:30	
12:00		12:00		12:00	
12:30		12:30		12:30	
1:00		1:00		1:00	
1:30		1:30		1:30	
2:00		2:00		2:00	
2:30		2:30		2:30	
3:00		3:00		3:00	
3:30		3:30		3:30	
4:00		4:00		4:00	
4:30		4:30		4:30	
5:00		5:00		5:00	
5:30		5:30		5:30	
6:00		6:00		6:00	
6:30		6:30		6:30	
7:00		7:00		7:00	
7:30		7:30		7:30	
8:00		8:00		8:00	
8:30		8:30		8:30	
9:00		9:00		9:00	
9:30		9:30		9:30	
10:00		10:00		10:00	
10:30		10:30		10:30	
11:00		11:00		11:00	

Ready for tomorrow?	( )	( )	( )
ALARM			
CLOTHES			
GLASS OF WATER			
SAVERS PREP			
BEDTIME AFFIRMATIONS			

Wednesday		Thursday		Friday		Saturday	
S		S		S		S	
A		A		A		A	
V		V		V		V	
E		E		E		E	
R		R		R		R	
S		S		S		S	
◆		◆		◆		◆	
◆		◆		◆		◆	
5:00		5:00		5:00		5:00	
5:30		5:30		5:30		5:30	
6:00		6:00		6:00		6:00	
6:30		6:30		6:30		6:30	
7:00		7:00		7:00		7:00	
7:30		7:30		7:30		7:30	
8:00		8:00		8:00		8:00	
8:30		8:30		8:30		8:30	
9:00		9:00		9:00		9:00	
9:30		9:30		9:30		9:30	
10:00		10:00		10:00		10:00	
10:30		10:30		10:30		10:30	
11:00		11:00		11:00		11:00	
11:30		11:30		11:30		11:30	
12:00		12:00		12:00		12:00	
12:30		12:30		12:30		12:30	
1:00		1:00		1:00		1:00	
1:30		1:30		1:30		1:30	
2:00		2:00		2:00		2:00	
2:30		2:30		2:30		2:30	
3:00		3:00		3:00		3:00	
3:30		3:30		3:30		3:30	
4:00		4:00		4:00		4:00	
4:30		4:30		4:30		4:30	
5:00		5:00		5:00		5:00	
5:30		5:30		5:30		5:30	
6:00		6:00		6:00		6:00	
6:30		6:30		6:30		6:30	
7:00		7:00		7:00		7:00	
7:30		7:30		7:30		7:30	
8:00		8:00		8:00		8:00	
8:30		8:30		8:30		8:30	
9:00		9:00		9:00		9:00	
9:30		9:30		9:30		9:30	
10:00		10:00		10:00		10:00	
10:30		10:30		10:30		10:30	
11:00		11:00		11:00		11:00	
	( )		( )		( )		( )

Week of:	Sunday	Monday	Tuesday
This Week's Goal	S	S	S
	A	A	A
	V	V	V
	E	E	E
	R	R	R
	S	S	S
Intention for the Day	◆	◆	◆
Grateful for ...	◆	◆	◆

Life is what happens to you while you're busy making other plans.

—JOHN LENNON

TO-DO LIST	Sunday	Monday	Tuesday
Highest Priority	5:00	5:00	5:00
	5:30	5:30	5:30
	6:00	6:00	6:00
	6:30	6:30	6:30
	7:00	7:00	7:00
	7:30	7:30	7:30
	8:00	8:00	8:00
	8:30	8:30	8:30
	9:00	9:00	9:00
	9:30	9:30	9:30
	10:00	10:00	10:00
	10:30	10:30	10:30
	11:00	11:00	11:00
	11:30	11:30	11:30
	12:00	12:00	12:00
	12:30	12:30	12:30
	1:00	1:00	1:00
Definite Priority	1:30	1:30	1:30
	2:00	2:00	2:00
	2:30	2:30	2:30
	3:00	3:00	3:00
	3:30	3:30	3:30
	4:00	4:00	4:00
Lowest Priority	4:30	4:30	4:30
	5:00	5:00	5:00
	5:30	5:30	5:30
	6:00	6:00	6:00
	6:30	6:30	6:30
	7:00	7:00	7:00
	7:30	7:30	7:30
Habit to Work on This Week	8:00	8:00	8:00
	8:30	8:30	8:30
	9:00	9:00	9:00
	9:30	9:30	9:30
	10:00	10:00	10:00
	10:30	10:30	10:30
	11:00	11:00	11:00

Ready for tomorrow?	( )	( )	( )
ALARM			
CLOTHES			
GLASS OF WATER			
SAVERS PREP			
BEDTIME AFFIRMATIONS			

Wednesday	Thursday	Friday	Saturday
S	S	S	S
A	A	A	A
V	V	V	V
E	E	E	E
R	R	R	R
S	S	S	S

◆	◆	◆	◆
◆	◆	◆	◆

Wednesday		Thursday		Friday		Saturday	
5:00		5:00		5:00		5:00	
5:30		5:30		5:30		5:30	
6:00		6:00		6:00		6:00	
6:30		6:30		6:30		6:30	
7:00		7:00		7:00		7:00	
7:30		7:30		7:30		7:30	
8:00		8:00		8:00		8:00	
8:30		8:30		8:30		8:30	
9:00		9:00		9:00		9:00	
9:30		9:30		9:30		9:30	
10:00		10:00		10:00		10:00	
10:30		10:30		10:30		10:30	
11:00		11:00		11:00		11:00	
11:30		11:30		11:30		11:30	
12:00		12:00		12:00		12:00	
12:30		12:30		12:30		12:30	
1:00		1:00		1:00		1:00	
1:30		1:30		1:30		1:30	
2:00		2:00		2:00		2:00	
2:30		2:30		2:30		2:30	
3:00		3:00		3:00		3:00	
3:30		3:30		3:30		3:30	
4:00		4:00		4:00		4:00	
4:30		4:30		4:30		4:30	
5:00		5:00		5:00		5:00	
5:30		5:30		5:30		5:30	
6:00		6:00		6:00		6:00	
6:30		6:30		6:30		6:30	
7:00		7:00		7:00		7:00	
7:30		7:30		7:30		7:30	
8:00		8:00		8:00		8:00	
8:30		8:30		8:30		8:30	
9:00		9:00		9:00		9:00	
9:30		9:30		9:30		9:30	
10:00		10:00		10:00		10:00	
10:30		10:30		10:30		10:30	
11:00		11:00		11:00		11:00	

( )	( )	( )	( )

Week of:	Sunday	Monday	Tuesday
This Week's Goal	S	S	S
	A	A	A
	V	V	V
	E	E	E
	R	R	R
	S	S	S
Intention for the Day	◆	◆	◆
Grateful for ...	◆	◆	◆

Your time is limited, so don't waste it living someone else's life.

—STEVE JOBS

TO-DO LIST

Highest Priority

Definite Priority

Lowest Priority

Habit to Work on This Week

Time	Sunday	Monday	Tuesday
5:00			
5:30			
6:00			
6:30			
7:00			
7:30			
8:00			
8:30			
9:00			
9:30			
10:00			
10:30			
11:00			
11:30			
12:00			
12:30			
1:00			
1:30			
2:00			
2:30			
3:00			
3:30			
4:00			
4:30			
5:00			
5:30			
6:00			
6:30			
7:00			
7:30			
8:00			
8:30			
9:00			
9:30			
10:00			
10:30			
11:00			

Ready for tomorrow?	( )	( )	( )
ALARM			
CLOTHES			
GLASS OF WATER			
SAVERS PREP			
BEDTIME AFFIRMATIONS			

Wednesday	Thursday	Friday	Saturday
S	S	S	S
A	A	A	A
V	V	V	V
E	E	E	E
R	R	R	R
S	S	S	S
◆	◆	◆	◆
◆	◆	◆	◆

Wednesday	Thursday	Friday	Saturday
5:00	5:00	5:00	5:00
5:30	5:30	5:30	5:30
6:00	6:00	6:00	6:00
6:30	6:30	6:30	6:30
7:00	7:00	7:00	7:00
7:30	7:30	7:30	7:30
8:00	8:00	8:00	8:00
8:30	8:30	8:30	8:30
9:00	9:00	9:00	9:00
9:30	9:30	9:30	9:30
10:00	10:00	10:00	10:00
10:30	10:30	10:30	10:30
11:00	11:00	11:00	11:00
11:30	11:30	11:30	11:30
12:00	12:00	12:00	12:00
12:30	12:30	12:30	12:30
1:00	1:00	1:00	1:00
1:30	1:30	1:30	1:30
2:00	2:00	2:00	2:00
2:30	2:30	2:30	2:30
3:00	3:00	3:00	3:00
3:30	3:30	3:30	3:30
4:00	4:00	4:00	4:00
4:30	4:30	4:30	4:30
5:00	5:00	5:00	5:00
5:30	5:30	5:30	5:30
6:00	6:00	6:00	6:00
6:30	6:30	6:30	6:30
7:00	7:00	7:00	7:00
7:30	7:30	7:30	7:30
8:00	8:00	8:00	8:00
8:30	8:30	8:30	8:30
9:00	9:00	9:00	9:00
9:30	9:30	9:30	9:30
10:00	10:00	10:00	10:00
10:30	10:30	10:30	10:30
11:00	11:00	11:00	11:00
( )	( )	( )	( )

Week of:	Sunday	Monday	Tuesday
This Week's Goal	S	S	S
	A	A	A
	V	V	V
	E	E	E
	R	R	R
	S	S	S
Intention for the Day	◆	◆	◆
Grateful for ...	◆	◆	◆

Life is 10% what happens to me and 90% of how I react to it.

–CHARLES SWINDOLL

TO-DO LIST	Sunday	Monday	Tuesday
Highest Priority	5:00	5:00	5:00
	5:30	5:30	5:30
	6:00	6:00	6:00
	6:30	6:30	6:30
	7:00	7:00	7:00
	7:30	7:30	7:30
	8:00	8:00	8:00
	8:30	8:30	8:30
	9:00	9:00	9:00
	9:30	9:30	9:30
	10:00	10:00	10:00
	10:30	10:30	10:30
	11:00	11:00	11:00
	11:30	11:30	11:30
	12:00	12:00	12:00
	12:30	12:30	12:30
	1:00	1:00	1:00
Definite Priority	1:30	1:30	1:30
	2:00	2:00	2:00
	2:30	2:30	2:30
	3:00	3:00	3:00
	3:30	3:30	3:30
	4:00	4:00	4:00
Lowest Priority	4:30	4:30	4:30
	5:00	5:00	5:00
	5:30	5:30	5:30
	6:00	6:00	6:00
	6:30	6:30	6:30
	7:00	7:00	7:00
	7:30	7:30	7:30
Habit to Work on This Week	8:00	8:00	8:00
	8:30	8:30	8:30
	9:00	9:00	9:00
	9:30	9:30	9:30
	10:00	10:00	10:00
	10:30	10:30	10:30
	11:00	11:00	11:00

Ready for tomorrow?	( )	( )	( )
ALARM			
CLOTHES			
GLASS OF WATER			
SAVERS PREP			
BEDTIME AFFIRMATIONS			

Wednesday		Thursday		Friday		Saturday	
S		S		S		S	
A		A		A		A	
V		V		V		V	
E		E		E		E	
R		R		R		R	
S		S		S		S	
◆		◆		◆		◆	
◆		◆		◆		◆	
5:00		5:00		5:00		5:00	
5:30		5:30		5:30		5:30	
6:00		6:00		6:00		6:00	
6:30		6:30		6:30		6:30	
7:00		7:00		7:00		7:00	
7:30		7:30		7:30		7:30	
8:00		8:00		8:00		8:00	
8:30		8:30		8:30		8:30	
9:00		9:00		9:00		9:00	
9:30		9:30		9:30		9:30	
10:00		10:00		10:00		10:00	
10:30		10:30		10:30		10:30	
11:00		11:00		11:00		11:00	
11:30		11:30		11:30		11:30	
12:00		12:00		12:00		12:00	
12:30		12:30		12:30		12:30	
1:00		1:00		1:00		1:00	
1:30		1:30		1:30		1:30	
2:00		2:00		2:00		2:00	
2:30		2:30		2:30		2:30	
3:00		3:00		3:00		3:00	
3:30		3:30		3:30		3:30	
4:00		4:00		4:00		4:00	
4:30		4:30		4:30		4:30	
5:00		5:00		5:00		5:00	
5:30		5:30		5:30		5:30	
6:00		6:00		6:00		6:00	
6:30		6:30		6:30		6:30	
7:00		7:00		7:00		7:00	
7:30		7:30		7:30		7:30	
8:00		8:00		8:00		8:00	
8:30		8:30		8:30		8:30	
9:00		9:00		9:00		9:00	
9:30		9:30		9:30		9:30	
10:00		10:00		10:00		10:00	
10:30		10:30		10:30		10:30	
11:00		11:00		11:00		11:00	
	( )		( )		( )		( )

MONTHLY REFLECTION

Write 5 things you accomplished this month:

1.

2.

3.

4.

5.

QUESTIONS

1) What did I learn about myself this month?

2) What tasks are left over from this month that are lingering and need to get done?

3. Did I take care of myself?

4) What could I have done differently this past month?

5) What areas can I (still) improve on?

6) What experiences can I treasure?

7) What challenged me and how did I overcome the challenge?

8) What specific habits and/or rituals could I develop this month to support my vision?

MONTH OF:	SUNDAY	MONDAY	TUESDAY
This Month's Goal			
Important Events or Reminders to Transfer to My Phone			
1.			
2.			
3.			
4.			
5.			
6.			
7.			
8.			
9.			
10.			

PROJECT NAME	TEAM PLAYERS	IMPORTANT DATES	DEADLINES
1.			
2.			
3.			
4.			

WEDNESDAY	THURSDAY	FRIDAY	SATURDAY

BRAINSTORM

Week of:	Sunday		Monday		Tuesday	
This Week's Goal	S		S		S	
	A		A		A	
	V		V		V	
	E		E		E	
	R		R		R	
	S		S		S	
Intention for the Day	◆		◆		◆	
Grateful for ...	◆		◆		◆	

	Sunday	Monday	Tuesday
The best time to plant a tree was 20 years ago. The second best time is now. **−CHINESE PROVERB**	5:00	5:00	5:00
	5:30	5:30	5:30
	6:00	6:00	6:00
	6:30	6:30	6:30
	7:00	7:00	7:00
	7:30	7:30	7:30
	8:00	8:00	8:00
	8:30	8:30	8:30
	9:00	9:00	9:00
	9:30	9:30	9:30
TO-DO LIST	10:00	10:00	10:00
Highest Priority	10:30	10:30	10:30
	11:00	11:00	11:00
	11:30	11:30	11:30
	12:00	12:00	12:00
	12:30	12:30	12:30
	1:00	1:00	1:00
Definite Priority	1:30	1:30	1:30
	2:00	2:00	2:00
	2:30	2:30	2:30
	3:00	3:00	3:00
	3:30	3:30	3:30
	4:00	4:00	4:00
Lowest Priority	4:30	4:30	4:30
	5:00	5:00	5:00
	5:30	5:30	5:30
	6:00	6:00	6:00
	6:30	6:30	6:30
	7:00	7:00	7:00
	7:30	7:30	7:30
Habit to Work on This Week	8:00	8:00	8:00
	8:30	8:30	8:30
	9:00	9:00	9:00
	9:30	9:30	9:30
	10:00	10:00	10:00
	10:30	10:30	10:30
	11:00	11:00	11:00

Ready for tomorrow?	( )	( )	( )
ALARM			
CLOTHES			
GLASS OF WATER			
SAVERS PREP			
BEDTIME AFFIRMATIONS			

Wednesday	Thursday	Friday	Saturday
S	S	S	S
A	A	A	A
V	V	V	V
E	E	E	E
R	R	R	R
S	S	S	S

◆	◆	◆	◆
◆	◆	◆	◆

Wednesday		Thursday		Friday		Saturday	
5:00		5:00		5:00		5:00	
5:30		5:30		5:30		5:30	
6:00		6:00		6:00		6:00	
6:30		6:30		6:30		6:30	
7:00		7:00		7:00		7:00	
7:30		7:30		7:30		7:30	
8:00		8:00		8:00		8:00	
8:30		8:30		8:30		8:30	
9:00		9:00		9:00		9:00	
9:30		9:30		9:30		9:30	
10:00		10:00		10:00		10:00	
10:30		10:30		10:30		10:30	
11:00		11:00		11:00		11:00	
11:30		11:30		11:30		11:30	
12:00		12:00		12:00		12:00	
12:30		12:30		12:30		12:30	
1:00		1:00		1:00		1:00	
1:30		1:30		1:30		1:30	
2:00		2:00		2:00		2:00	
2:30		2:30		2:30		2:30	
3:00		3:00		3:00		3:00	
3:30		3:30		3:30		3:30	
4:00		4:00		4:00		4:00	
4:30		4:30		4:30		4:30	
5:00		5:00		5:00		5:00	
5:30		5:30		5:30		5:30	
6:00		6:00		6:00		6:00	
6:30		6:30		6:30		6:30	
7:00		7:00		7:00		7:00	
7:30		7:30		7:30		7:30	
8:00		8:00		8:00		8:00	
8:30		8:30		8:30		8:30	
9:00		9:00		9:00		9:00	
9:30		9:30		9:30		9:30	
10:00		10:00		10:00		10:00	
10:30		10:30		10:30		10:30	
11:00		11:00		11:00		11:00	
	( )		( )		( )		( )

Week of:	Sunday	Monday	Tuesday
This Week's Goal	S	S	S
	A	A	A
	V	V	V
	E	E	E
	R	R	R
	S	S	S
Intention for the Day	◆	◆	◆
Grateful for ...	◆	◆	◆

I've learned that people will forget what you said, people will forget what you did, but people will never forget how you made them feel.

—**MAYA ANGELOU**

TO-DO LIST	Sunday	Monday	Tuesday
Highest Priority	5:00	5:00	5:00
	5:30	5:30	5:30
	6:00	6:00	6:00
	6:30	6:30	6:30
	7:00	7:00	7:00
	7:30	7:30	7:30
	8:00	8:00	8:00
	8:30	8:30	8:30
	9:00	9:00	9:00
	9:30	9:30	9:30
	10:00	10:00	10:00
	10:30	10:30	10:30
	11:00	11:00	11:00
	11:30	11:30	11:30
	12:00	12:00	12:00
	12:30	12:30	12:30
	1:00	1:00	1:00
Definite Priority	1:30	1:30	1:30
	2:00	2:00	2:00
	2:30	2:30	2:30
	3:00	3:00	3:00
	3:30	3:30	3:30
	4:00	4:00	4:00
Lowest Priority	4:30	4:30	4:30
	5:00	5:00	5:00
	5:30	5:30	5:30
	6:00	6:00	6:00
	6:30	6:30	6:30
	7:00	7:00	7:00
	7:30	7:30	7:30
Habit to Work on This Week	8:00	8:00	8:00
	8:30	8:30	8:30
	9:00	9:00	9:00
	9:30	9:30	9:30
	10:00	10:00	10:00
	10:30	10:30	10:30
	11:00	11:00	11:00

Ready for tomorrow?	( )	( )	( )
ALARM			
CLOTHES			
GLASS OF WATER			
SAVERS PREP			
BEDTIME AFFIRMATIONS			

Wednesday		Thursday		Friday		Saturday	
S		S		S		S	
A		A		A		A	
V		V		V		V	
E		E		E		E	
R		R		R		R	
S		S		S		S	
◆		◆		◆		◆	
◆		◆		◆		◆	
5:00		5:00		5:00		5:00	
5:30		5:30		5:30		5:30	
6:00		6:00		6:00		6:00	
6:30		6:30		6:30		6:30	
7:00		7:00		7:00		7:00	
7:30		7:30		7:30		7:30	
8:00		8:00		8:00		8:00	
8:30		8:30		8:30		8:30	
9:00		9:00		9:00		9:00	
9:30		9:30		9:30		9:30	
10:00		10:00		10:00		10:00	
10:30		10:30		10:30		10:30	
11:00		11:00		11:00		11:00	
11:30		11:30		11:30		11:30	
12:00		12:00		12:00		12:00	
12:30		12:30		12:30		12:30	
1:00		1:00		1:00		1:00	
1:30		1:30		1:30		1:30	
2:00		2:00		2:00		2:00	
2:30		2:30		2:30		2:30	
3:00		3:00		3:00		3:00	
3:30		3:30		3:30		3:30	
4:00		4:00		4:00		4:00	
4:30		4:30		4:30		4:30	
5:00		5:00		5:00		5:00	
5:30		5:30		5:30		5:30	
6:00		6:00		6:00		6:00	
6:30		6:30		6:30		6:30	
7:00		7:00		7:00		7:00	
7:30		7:30		7:30		7:30	
8:00		8:00		8:00		8:00	
8:30		8:30		8:30		8:30	
9:00		9:00		9:00		9:00	
9:30		9:30		9:30		9:30	
10:00		10:00		10:00		10:00	
10:30		10:30		10:30		10:30	
11:00		11:00		11:00		11:00	
	( )		( )		( )		( )

Week of:	Sunday		Monday		Tuesday	
This Week's Goal	S		S		S	
	A		A		A	
	V		V		V	
	E		E		E	
	R		R		R	
	S		S		S	
Intention for the Day	◆		◆		◆	
Grateful for ...	◆		◆		◆	

Nothing will prove to be your greatest teacher more than your failures. So keep trying, keep succeeding, and keep failing. There is something to learn in all those experiences.

—NATALIE JANJI

TO-DO LIST
Highest Priority
Definite Priority
Lowest Priority
Habit to Work on This Week

	Sunday	Monday	Tuesday
5:00		5:00	5:00
5:30		5:30	5:30
6:00		6:00	6:00
6:30		6:30	6:30
7:00		7:00	7:00
7:30		7:30	7:30
8:00		8:00	8:00
8:30		8:30	8:30
9:00		9:00	9:00
9:30		9:30	9:30
10:00		10:00	10:00
10:30		10:30	10:30
11:00		11:00	11:00
11:30		11:30	11:30
12:00		12:00	12:00
12:30		12:30	12:30
1:00		1:00	1:00
1:30		1:30	1:30
2:00		2:00	2:00
2:30		2:30	2:30
3:00		3:00	3:00
3:30		3:30	3:30
4:00		4:00	4:00
4:30		4:30	4:30
5:00		5:00	5:00
5:30		5:30	5:30
6:00		6:00	6:00
6:30		6:30	6:30
7:00		7:00	7:00
7:30		7:30	7:30
8:00		8:00	8:00
8:30		8:30	8:30
9:00		9:00	9:00
9:30		9:30	9:30
10:00		10:00	10:00
10:30		10:30	10:30
11:00		11:00	11:00

Ready for tomorrow?	( )	( )	( )
ALARM			
CLOTHES			
GLASS OF WATER			
SAVERS PREP			
BEDTIME AFFIRMATIONS			

Wednesday		Thursday		Friday		Saturday	
S		S		S		S	
A		A		A		A	
V		V		V		V	
E		E		E		E	
R		R		R		R	
S		S		S		S	
◆		◆		◆		◆	
◆		◆		◆		◆	
5:00		5:00		5:00		5:00	
5:30		5:30		5:30		5:30	
6:00		6:00		6:00		6:00	
6:30		6:30		6:30		6:30	
7:00		7:00		7:00		7:00	
7:30		7:30		7:30		7:30	
8:00		8:00		8:00		8:00	
8:30		8:30		8:30		8:30	
9:00		9:00		9:00		9:00	
9:30		9:30		9:30		9:30	
10:00		10:00		10:00		10:00	
10:30		10:30		10:30		10:30	
11:00		11:00		11:00		11:00	
11:30		11:30		11:30		11:30	
12:00		12:00		12:00		12:00	
12:30		12:30		12:30		12:30	
1:00		1:00		1:00		1:00	
1:30		1:30		1:30		1:30	
2:00		2:00		2:00		2:00	
2:30		2:30		2:30		2:30	
3:00		3:00		3:00		3:00	
3:30		3:30		3:30		3:30	
4:00		4:00		4:00		4:00	
4:30		4:30		4:30		4:30	
5:00		5:00		5:00		5:00	
5:30		5:30		5:30		5:30	
6:00		6:00		6:00		6:00	
6:30		6:30		6:30		6:30	
7:00		7:00		7:00		7:00	
7:30		7:30		7:30		7:30	
8:00		8:00		8:00		8:00	
8:30		8:30		8:30		8:30	
9:00		9:00		9:00		9:00	
9:30		9:30		9:30		9:30	
10:00		10:00		10:00		10:00	
10:30		10:30		10:30		10:30	
11:00		11:00		11:00		11:00	
	( )		( )		( )		( )

Week of:	Sunday		Monday		Tuesday	
This Week's Goal	S		S		S	
	A		A		A	
	V		V		V	
	E		E		E	
	R		R		R	
	S		S		S	
Intention for the Day	◆		◆		◆	
Grateful for ...	◆		◆		◆	

	Sunday	Monday	Tuesday
	5:00	5:00	5:00
	5:30	5:30	5:30
Whatever you think is	6:00	6:00	6:00
possible is possible with	6:30	6:30	6:30
the right plan and the	7:00	7:00	7:00
right actions.	7:30	7:30	7:30
	8:00	8:00	8:00
—HONORÉE CORDER	8:30	8:30	8:30
	9:00	9:00	9:00
	9:30	9:30	9:30
TO-DO LIST	10:00	10:00	10:00
Highest Priority	10:30	10:30	10:30
	11:00	11:00	11:00
	11:30	11:30	11:30
	12:00	12:00	12:00
	12:30	12:30	12:30
	1:00	1:00	1:00
Definite Priority	1:30	1:30	1:30
	2:00	2:00	2:00
	2:30	2:30	2:30
	3:00	3:00	3:00
	3:30	3:30	3:30
	4:00	4:00	4:00
Lowest Priority	4:30	4:30	4:30
	5:00	5:00	5:00
	5:30	5:30	5:30
	6:00	6:00	6:00
	6:30	6:30	6:30
	7:00	7:00	7:00
	7:30	7:30	7:30
Habit to Work on This Week	8:00	8:00	8:00
	8:30	8:30	8:30
	9:00	9:00	9:00
	9:30	9:30	9:30
	10:00	10:00	10:00
	10:30	10:30	10:30
	11:00	11:00	11:00

Ready for tomorrow?	( )	( )	( )
ALARM			
CLOTHES			
GLASS OF WATER			
SAVERS PREP			
BEDTIME AFFIRMATIONS			

Wednesday	Thursday	Friday	Saturday
S	S	S	S
A	A	A	A
V	V	V	V
E	E	E	E
R	R	R	R
S	S	S	S
◆	◆	◆	◆
◆	◆	◆	◆

Wednesday		Thursday		Friday		Saturday	
5:00		5:00		5:00		5:00	
5:30		5:30		5:30		5:30	
6:00		6:00		6:00		6:00	
6:30		6:30		6:30		6:30	
7:00		7:00		7:00		7:00	
7:30		7:30		7:30		7:30	
8:00		8:00		8:00		8:00	
8:30		8:30		8:30		8:30	
9:00		9:00		9:00		9:00	
9:30		9:30		9:30		9:30	
10:00		10:00		10:00		10:00	
10:30		10:30		10:30		10:30	
11:00		11:00		11:00		11:00	
11:30		11:30		11:30		11:30	
12:00		12:00		12:00		12:00	
12:30		12:30		12:30		12:30	
1:00		1:00		1:00		1:00	
1:30		1:30		1:30		1:30	
2:00		2:00		2:00		2:00	
2:30		2:30		2:30		2:30	
3:00		3:00		3:00		3:00	
3:30		3:30		3:30		3:30	
4:00		4:00		4:00		4:00	
4:30		4:30		4:30		4:30	
5:00		5:00		5:00		5:00	
5:30		5:30		5:30		5:30	
6:00		6:00		6:00		6:00	
6:30		6:30		6:30		6:30	
7:00		7:00		7:00		7:00	
7:30		7:30		7:30		7:30	
8:00		8:00		8:00		8:00	
8:30		8:30		8:30		8:30	
9:00		9:00		9:00		9:00	
9:30		9:30		9:30		9:30	
10:00		10:00		10:00		10:00	
10:30		10:30		10:30		10:30	
11:00		11:00		11:00		11:00	
	( )		( )		( )		( )

Week of:	Sunday		Monday		Tuesday	
This Week's Goal	S		S		S	
	A		A		A	
	V		V		V	
	E		E		E	
	R		R		R	
	S		S		S	
Intention for the Day	◆		◆		◆	
Grateful for ...	◆		◆		◆	

How wonderful it is that nobody need wait a single moment before starting to improve the world.

—ANNE FRANK

TO-DO LIST			
Highest Priority			
Definite Priority			
Lowest Priority			
Habit to Work on This Week			

	Sunday	Monday	Tuesday
5:00		5:00	5:00
5:30		5:30	5:30
6:00		6:00	6:00
6:30		6:30	6:30
7:00		7:00	7:00
7:30		7:30	7:30
8:00		8:00	8:00
8:30		8:30	8:30
9:00		9:00	9:00
9:30		9:30	9:30
10:00		10:00	10:00
10:30		10:30	10:30
11:00		11:00	11:00
11:30		11:30	11:30
12:00		12:00	12:00
12:30		12:30	12:30
1:00		1:00	1:00
1:30		1:30	1:30
2:00		2:00	2:00
2:30		2:30	2:30
3:00		3:00	3:00
3:30		3:30	3:30
4:00		4:00	4:00
4:30		4:30	4:30
5:00		5:00	5:00
5:30		5:30	5:30
6:00		6:00	6:00
6:30		6:30	6:30
7:00		7:00	7:00
7:30		7:30	7:30
8:00		8:00	8:00
8:30		8:30	8:30
9:00		9:00	9:00
9:30		9:30	9:30
10:00		10:00	10:00
10:30		10:30	10:30
11:00		11:00	11:00

Ready for tomorrow?	( )	( )	( )
ALARM			
CLOTHES			
GLASS OF WATER			
SAVERS PREP			
BEDTIME AFFIRMATIONS			

Wednesday	Thursday	Friday	Saturday
S	S	S	S
A	A	A	A
V	V	V	V
E	E	E	E
R	R	R	R
S	S	S	S

◆	◆	◆	◆
◆	◆	◆	◆

Wednesday		Thursday		Friday		Saturday	
5:00		5:00		5:00		5:00	
5:30		5:30		5:30		5:30	
6:00		6:00		6:00		6:00	
6:30		6:30		6:30		6:30	
7:00		7:00		7:00		7:00	
7:30		7:30		7:30		7:30	
8:00		8:00		8:00		8:00	
8:30		8:30		8:30		8:30	
9:00		9:00		9:00		9:00	
9:30		9:30		9:30		9:30	
10:00		10:00		10:00		10:00	
10:30		10:30		10:30		10:30	
11:00		11:00		11:00		11:00	
11:30		11:30		11:30		11:30	
12:00		12:00		12:00		12:00	
12:30		12:30		12:30		12:30	
1:00		1:00		1:00		1:00	
1:30		1:30		1:30		1:30	
2:00		2:00		2:00		2:00	
2:30		2:30		2:30		2:30	
3:00		3:00		3:00		3:00	
3:30		3:30		3:30		3:30	
4:00		4:00		4:00		4:00	
4:30		4:30		4:30		4:30	
5:00		5:00		5:00		5:00	
5:30		5:30		5:30		5:30	
6:00		6:00		6:00		6:00	
6:30		6:30		6:30		6:30	
7:00		7:00		7:00		7:00	
7:30		7:30		7:30		7:30	
8:00		8:00		8:00		8:00	
8:30		8:30		8:30		8:30	
9:00		9:00		9:00		9:00	
9:30		9:30		9:30		9:30	
10:00		10:00		10:00		10:00	
10:30		10:30		10:30		10:30	
11:00		11:00		11:00		11:00	

( )	( )	( )	( )

MONTHLY REFLECTION

· ·

Write 5 things you accomplished this month:

1.

2.

3.

4.

5.

QUESTIONS

1) What did I learn about myself this month?

2) What tasks are left over from this month that are lingering and need to get done?

3. Did I take care of myself?

4) What could I have done differently this past month?

5) What areas can I (still) improve on?

6) What experiences can I treasure?

7) What challenged me and how did I overcome the challenge?

8) What specific habits and/or rituals could I develop this month to support my vision?

MONTH OF:	SUNDAY	MONDAY	TUESDAY
This Month's Goal			
Important Events or Reminders to Transfer to My Phone 1. 2. 3. 4. 5. 6. 7. 8. 9. 10.			

PROJECT NAME	TEAM PLAYERS	IMPORTANT DATES	DEADLINES
1.			
2.			
3.			
4.			

WEDNESDAY	THURSDAY	FRIDAY	SATURDAY

BRAINSTORM

Week of:	Sunday	Monday	Tuesday
This Week's Goal	S	S	S
	A	A	A
	V	V	V
	E	E	E
	R	R	R
	S	S	S
Intention for the Day	◆	◆	◆
Grateful for ...	◆	◆	◆

Success is going from failure to failure without losing your enthusiasm.

–WINSTON CHURCHILL

TO-DO LIST		
Highest Priority		
Definite Priority		
Lowest Priority		
Habit to Work on This Week		

Time	Sunday	Monday	Tuesday
5:00			
5:30			
6:00			
6:30			
7:00			
7:30			
8:00			
8:30			
9:00			
9:30			
10:00			
10:30			
11:00			
11:30			
12:00			
12:30			
1:00			
1:30			
2:00			
2:30			
3:00			
3:30			
4:00			
4:30			
5:00			
5:30			
6:00			
6:30			
7:00			
7:30			
8:00			
8:30			
9:00			
9:30			
10:00			
10:30			
11:00			

Ready for tomorrow?	( )	( )	( )
ALARM			
CLOTHES			
GLASS OF WATER			
SAVERS PREP			
BEDTIME AFFIRMATIONS			

Wednesday	Thursday	Friday	Saturday
S	S	S	S
A	A	A	A
V	V	V	V
E	E	E	E
R	R	R	R
S	S	S	S
◆	◆	◆	◆
◆	◆	◆	◆

Wednesday		Thursday		Friday		Saturday	
5:00		5:00		5:00		5:00	
5:30		5:30		5:30		5:30	
6:00		6:00		6:00		6:00	
6:30		6:30		6:30		6:30	
7:00		7:00		7:00		7:00	
7:30		7:30		7:30		7:30	
8:00		8:00		8:00		8:00	
8:30		8:30		8:30		8:30	
9:00		9:00		9:00		9:00	
9:30		9:30		9:30		9:30	
10:00		10:00		10:00		10:00	
10:30		10:30		10:30		10:30	
11:00		11:00		11:00		11:00	
11:30		11:30		11:30		11:30	
12:00		12:00		12:00		12:00	
12:30		12:30		12:30		12:30	
1:00		1:00		1:00		1:00	
1:30		1:30		1:30		1:30	
2:00		2:00		2:00		2:00	
2:30		2:30		2:30		2:30	
3:00		3:00		3:00		3:00	
3:30		3:30		3:30		3:30	
4:00		4:00		4:00		4:00	
4:30		4:30		4:30		4:30	
5:00		5:00		5:00		5:00	
5:30		5:30		5:30		5:30	
6:00		6:00		6:00		6:00	
6:30		6:30		6:30		6:30	
7:00		7:00		7:00		7:00	
7:30		7:30		7:30		7:30	
8:00		8:00		8:00		8:00	
8:30		8:30		8:30		8:30	
9:00		9:00		9:00		9:00	
9:30		9:30		9:30		9:30	
10:00		10:00		10:00		10:00	
10:30		10:30		10:30		10:30	
11:00		11:00		11:00		11:00	
( )		( )		( )		( )	

Week of:	Sunday		Monday		Tuesday	
This Week's Goal	S		S		S	
	A		A		A	
	V		V		V	
	E		E		E	
	R		R		R	
	S		S		S	

Intention for the Day	◆	◆	◆
Grateful for ...	◆	◆	◆

Dream big and dare to fail.

–NORMAN VAUGHAN

TO-DO LIST
Highest Priority

Sunday	Monday	Tuesday
5:00	5:00	5:00
5:30	5:30	5:30
6:00	6:00	6:00
6:30	6:30	6:30
7:00	7:00	7:00
7:30	7:30	7:30
8:00	8:00	8:00
8:30	8:30	8:30
9:00	9:00	9:00
9:30	9:30	9:30
10:00	10:00	10:00
10:30	10:30	10:30
11:00	11:00	11:00
11:30	11:30	11:30
12:00	12:00	12:00
12:30	12:30	12:30
1:00	1:00	1:00
1:30	1:30	1:30
2:00	2:00	2:00
2:30	2:30	2:30
3:00	3:00	3:00
3:30	3:30	3:30
4:00	4:00	4:00
4:30	4:30	4:30
5:00	5:00	5:00
5:30	5:30	5:30
6:00	6:00	6:00
6:30	6:30	6:30
7:00	7:00	7:00
7:30	7:30	7:30
8:00	8:00	8:00
8:30	8:30	8:30
9:00	9:00	9:00
9:30	9:30	9:30
10:00	10:00	10:00
10:30	10:30	10:30
11:00	11:00	11:00

Definite Priority

Lowest Priority

Habit to Work on This Week

Ready for tomorrow?	( )	( )	( )
ALARM			
CLOTHES			
GLASS OF WATER			
SAVERS PREP			
BEDTIME AFFIRMATIONS			

Wednesday		Thursday		Friday		Saturday	
S		S		S		S	
A		A		A		A	
V		V		V		V	
E		E		E		E	
R		R		R		R	
S		S		S		S	
◆		◆		◆		◆	
◆		◆		◆		◆	
5:00		5:00		5:00		5:00	
5:30		5:30		5:30		5:30	
6:00		6:00		6:00		6:00	
6:30		6:30		6:30		6:30	
7:00		7:00		7:00		7:00	
7:30		7:30		7:30		7:30	
8:00		8:00		8:00		8:00	
8:30		8:30		8:30		8:30	
9:00		9:00		9:00		9:00	
9:30		9:30		9:30		9:30	
10:00		10:00		10:00		10:00	
10:30		10:30		10:30		10:30	
11:00		11:00		11:00		11:00	
11:30		11:30		11:30		11:30	
12:00		12:00		12:00		12:00	
12:30		12:30		12:30		12:30	
1:00		1:00		1:00		1:00	
1:30		1:30		1:30		1:30	
2:00		2:00		2:00		2:00	
2:30		2:30		2:30		2:30	
3:00		3:00		3:00		3:00	
3:30		3:30		3:30		3:30	
4:00		4:00		4:00		4:00	
4:30		4:30		4:30		4:30	
5:00		5:00		5:00		5:00	
5:30		5:30		5:30		5:30	
6:00		6:00		6:00		6:00	
6:30		6:30		6:30		6:30	
7:00		7:00		7:00		7:00	
7:30		7:30		7:30		7:30	
8:00		8:00		8:00		8:00	
8:30		8:30		8:30		8:30	
9:00		9:00		9:00		9:00	
9:30		9:30		9:30		9:30	
10:00		10:00		10:00		10:00	
10:30		10:30		10:30		10:30	
11:00		11:00		11:00		11:00	
( )		( )		( )		( )	

Week of:	Sunday	Monday	Tuesday
This Week's Goal	S	S	S
	A	A	A
	V	V	V
	E	E	E
	R	R	R
	S	S	S
Intention for the Day	◆	◆	◆
Grateful for ...	◆	◆	◆

You must be the change you wish to see in the world.

—GANDHI

	Sunday	Monday	Tuesday
TO-DO LIST	5:00	5:00	5:00
Highest Priority	5:30	5:30	5:30
	6:00	6:00	6:00
	6:30	6:30	6:30
	7:00	7:00	7:00
	7:30	7:30	7:30
	8:00	8:00	8:00
	8:30	8:30	8:30
	9:00	9:00	9:00
	9:30	9:30	9:30
	10:00	10:00	10:00
	10:30	10:30	10:30
	11:00	11:00	11:00
	11:30	11:30	11:30
	12:00	12:00	12:00
	12:30	12:30	12:30
	1:00	1:00	1:00
Definite Priority	1:30	1:30	1:30
	2:00	2:00	2:00
	2:30	2:30	2:30
	3:00	3:00	3:00
	3:30	3:30	3:30
	4:00	4:00	4:00
Lowest Priority	4:30	4:30	4:30
	5:00	5:00	5:00
	5:30	5:30	5:30
	6:00	6:00	6:00
	6:30	6:30	6:30
	7:00	7:00	7:00
	7:30	7:30	7:30
Habit to Work on This Week	8:00	8:00	8:00
	8:30	8:30	8:30
	9:00	9:00	9:00
	9:30	9:30	9:30
	10:00	10:00	10:00
	10:30	10:30	10:30
	11:00	11:00	11:00

Ready for tomorrow?	( )	( )	( )
ALARM			
CLOTHES			
GLASS OF WATER			
SAVERS PREP			
BEDTIME AFFIRMATIONS			

Wednesday	Thursday	Friday	Saturday
S	S	S	S
A	A	A	A
V	V	V	V
E	E	E	E
R	R	R	R
S	S	S	S
◆	◆	◆	◆
◆	◆	◆	◆

Wednesday		Thursday		Friday		Saturday	
5:00		5:00		5:00		5:00	
5:30		5:30		5:30		5:30	
6:00		6:00		6:00		6:00	
6:30		6:30		6:30		6:30	
7:00		7:00		7:00		7:00	
7:30		7:30		7:30		7:30	
8:00		8:00		8:00		8:00	
8:30		8:30		8:30		8:30	
9:00		9:00		9:00		9:00	
9:30		9:30		9:30		9:30	
10:00		10:00		10:00		10:00	
10:30		10:30		10:30		10:30	
11:00		11:00		11:00		11:00	
11:30		11:30		11:30		11:30	
12:00		12:00		12:00		12:00	
12:30		12:30		12:30		12:30	
1:00		1:00		1:00		1:00	
1:30		1:30		1:30		1:30	
2:00		2:00		2:00		2:00	
2:30		2:30		2:30		2:30	
3:00		3:00		3:00		3:00	
3:30		3:30		3:30		3:30	
4:00		4:00		4:00		4:00	
4:30		4:30		4:30		4:30	
5:00		5:00		5:00		5:00	
5:30		5:30		5:30		5:30	
6:00		6:00		6:00		6:00	
6:30		6:30		6:30		6:30	
7:00		7:00		7:00		7:00	
7:30		7:30		7:30		7:30	
8:00		8:00		8:00		8:00	
8:30		8:30		8:30		8:30	
9:00		9:00		9:00		9:00	
9:30		9:30		9:30		9:30	
10:00		10:00		10:00		10:00	
10:30		10:30		10:30		10:30	
11:00		11:00		11:00		11:00	
( )		( )		( )		( )	

Week of:	Sunday		Monday		Tuesday	
This Week's Goal	S		S		S	
	A		A		A	
	V		V		V	
	E		E		E	
	R		R		R	
	S		S		S	
Intention for the Day	◆		◆		◆	
Grateful for ...	◆		◆		◆	

Keep your face to the sunshine and you can never see the shadow.

—HELEN KELLER

TO-DO LIST		Sunday		Monday		Tuesday
Highest Priority	5:00		5:00		5:00	
	5:30		5:30		5:30	
	6:00		6:00		6:00	
	6:30		6:30		6:30	
	7:00		7:00		7:00	
	7:30		7:30		7:30	
	8:00		8:00		8:00	
	8:30		8:30		8:30	
	9:00		9:00		9:00	
	9:30		9:30		9:30	
	10:00		10:00		10:00	
	10:30		10:30		10:30	
	11:00		11:00		11:00	
	11:30		11:30		11:30	
	12:00		12:00		12:00	
	12:30		12:30		12:30	
	1:00		1:00		1:00	
Definite Priority	1:30		1:30		1:30	
	2:00		2:00		2:00	
	2:30		2:30		2:30	
	3:00		3:00		3:00	
	3:30		3:30		3:30	
	4:00		4:00		4:00	
Lowest Priority	4:30		4:30		4:30	
	5:00		5:00		5:00	
	5:30		5:30		5:30	
	6:00		6:00		6:00	
	6:30		6:30		6:30	
	7:00		7:00		7:00	
	7:30		7:30		7:30	
Habit to Work on This Week	8:00		8:00		8:00	
	8:30		8:30		8:30	
	9:00		9:00		9:00	
	9:30		9:30		9:30	
	10:00		10:00		10:00	
	10:30		10:30		10:30	
	11:00		11:00		11:00	

Ready for tomorrow?	( )	( )	( )
ALARM			
CLOTHES			
GLASS OF WATER			
SAVERS PREP			
BEDTIME AFFIRMATIONS			

Wednesday		Thursday		Friday		Saturday	
S		S		S		S	
A		A		A		A	
V		V		V		V	
E		E		E		E	
R		R		R		R	
S		S		S		S	
◆		◆		◆		◆	
◆		◆		◆		◆	
5:00		5:00		5:00		5:00	
5:30		5:30		5:30		5:30	
6:00		6:00		6:00		6:00	
6:30		6:30		6:30		6:30	
7:00		7:00		7:00		7:00	
7:30		7:30		7:30		7:30	
8:00		8:00		8:00		8:00	
8:30		8:30		8:30		8:30	
9:00		9:00		9:00		9:00	
9:30		9:30		9:30		9:30	
10:00		10:00		10:00		10:00	
10:30		10:30		10:30		10:30	
11:00		11:00		11:00		11:00	
11:30		11:30		11:30		11:30	
12:00		12:00		12:00		12:00	
12:30		12:30		12:30		12:30	
1:00		1:00		1:00		1:00	
1:30		1:30		1:30		1:30	
2:00		2:00		2:00		2:00	
2:30		2:30		2:30		2:30	
3:00		3:00		3:00		3:00	
3:30		3:30		3:30		3:30	
4:00		4:00		4:00		4:00	
4:30		4:30		4:30		4:30	
5:00		5:00		5:00		5:00	
5:30		5:30		5:30		5:30	
6:00		6:00		6:00		6:00	
6:30		6:30		6:30		6:30	
7:00		7:00		7:00		7:00	
7:30		7:30		7:30		7:30	
8:00		8:00		8:00		8:00	
8:30		8:30		8:30		8:30	
9:00		9:00		9:00		9:00	
9:30		9:30		9:30		9:30	
10:00		10:00		10:00		10:00	
10:30		10:30		10:30		10:30	
11:00		11:00		11:00		11:00	
	( )		( )		( )		( )

Week of:	Sunday	Monday	Tuesday
This Week's Goal	S	S	S
	A	A	A
	V	V	V
	E	E	E
	R	R	R
	S	S	S
Intention for the Day	◆	◆	◆
Grateful for ...	◆	◆	◆

Every strike brings me closer to the next home run.

—**BABE RUTH**

TO-DO LIST
Highest Priority
Definite Priority
Lowest Priority
Habit to Work on This Week

	Sunday	Monday	Tuesday
5:00		5:00		5:00	
5:30		5:30		5:30	
6:00		6:00		6:00	
6:30		6:30		6:30	
7:00		7:00		7:00	
7:30		7:30		7:30	
8:00		8:00		8:00	
8:30		8:30		8:30	
9:00		9:00		9:00	
9:30		9:30		9:30	
10:00		10:00		10:00	
10:30		10:30		10:30	
11:00		11:00		11:00	
11:30		11:30		11:30	
12:00		12:00		12:00	
12:30		12:30		12:30	
1:00		1:00		1:00	
1:30		1:30		1:30	
2:00		2:00		2:00	
2:30		2:30		2:30	
3:00		3:00		3:00	
3:30		3:30		3:30	
4:00		4:00		4:00	
4:30		4:30		4:30	
5:00		5:00		5:00	
5:30		5:30		5:30	
6:00		6:00		6:00	
6:30		6:30		6:30	
7:00		7:00		7:00	
7:30		7:30		7:30	
8:00		8:00		8:00	
8:30		8:30		8:30	
9:00		9:00		9:00	
9:30		9:30		9:30	
10:00		10:00		10:00	
10:30		10:30		10:30	
11:00		11:00		11:00	

Ready for tomorrow?	( )	( )	( )
ALARM			
CLOTHES			
GLASS OF WATER			
SAVERS PREP			
BEDTIME AFFIRMATIONS			

Wednesday		Thursday		Friday		Saturday	
S		S		S		S	
A		A		A		A	
V		V		V		V	
E		E		E		E	
R		R		R		R	
S		S		S		S	
◆		◆		◆		◆	
◆		◆		◆		◆	
5:00		5:00		5:00		5:00	
5:30		5:30		5:30		5:30	
6:00		6:00		6:00		6:00	
6:30		6:30		6:30		6:30	
7:00		7:00		7:00		7:00	
7:30		7:30		7:30		7:30	
8:00		8:00		8:00		8:00	
8:30		8:30		8:30		8:30	
9:00		9:00		9:00		9:00	
9:30		9:30		9:30		9:30	
10:00		10:00		10:00		10:00	
10:30		10:30		10:30		10:30	
11:00		11:00		11:00		11:00	
11:30		11:30		11:30		11:30	
12:00		12:00		12:00		12:00	
12:30		12:30		12:30		12:30	
1:00		1:00		1:00		1:00	
1:30		1:30		1:30		1:30	
2:00		2:00		2:00		2:00	
2:30		2:30		2:30		2:30	
3:00		3:00		3:00		3:00	
3:30		3:30		3:30		3:30	
4:00		4:00		4:00		4:00	
4:30		4:30		4:30		4:30	
5:00		5:00		5:00		5:00	
5:30		5:30		5:30		5:30	
6:00		6:00		6:00		6:00	
6:30		6:30		6:30		6:30	
7:00		7:00		7:00		7:00	
7:30		7:30		7:30		7:30	
8:00		8:00		8:00		8:00	
8:30		8:30		8:30		8:30	
9:00		9:00		9:00		9:00	
9:30		9:30		9:30		9:30	
10:00		10:00		10:00		10:00	
10:30		10:30		10:30		10:30	
11:00		11:00		11:00		11:00	
	( )		( )		( )		( )

MONTHLY REFLECTION

· ·

Write 5 things you accomplished this month:

1.

2.

3.

4.

5.

QUESTIONS

1) What did I learn about myself this month?

2) What tasks are left over from this month that are lingering and need to get done?

3. Did I take care of myself?

4) What could I have done differently this past month?

5) What areas can I (still) improve on?

6) What experiences can I treasure?

7) What challenged me and how did I overcome the challenge?

8) What specific habits and/or rituals could I develop this month to support my vision?

MONTH OF:	SUNDAY	MONDAY	TUESDAY
This Month's Goal			
Important Events or Reminders to Transfer to My Phone			
1.			
2.			
3.			
4.			
5.			
6.			
7.			
8.			
9.			
10.			

PROJECT NAME	TEAM PLAYERS	IMPORTANT DATES	DEADLINES
1.			
2.			
3.			
4.			

WEDNESDAY	THURSDAY	FRIDAY	SATURDAY

BRAINSTORM

Week of:	Sunday	Monday	Tuesday
This Week's Goal	S	S	S
	A	A	A
	V	V	V
	E	E	E
	R	R	R
	S	S	S
Intention for the Day	◆	◆	◆
Grateful for ...	◆	◆	◆

Don't wait. The time will never be just right.

—NAPOLEON HILL

TO-DO LIST
Highest Priority

Definite Priority

Lowest Priority

Habit to Work on This Week

Time	Sunday	Monday	Tuesday
5:00		5:00	5:00
5:30		5:30	5:30
6:00		6:00	6:00
6:30		6:30	6:30
7:00		7:00	7:00
7:30		7:30	7:30
8:00		8:00	8:00
8:30		8:30	8:30
9:00		9:00	9:00
9:30		9:30	9:30
10:00		10:00	10:00
10:30		10:30	10:30
11:00		11:00	11:00
11:30		11:30	11:30
12:00		12:00	12:00
12:30		12:30	12:30
1:00		1:00	1:00
1:30		1:30	1:30
2:00		2:00	2:00
2:30		2:30	2:30
3:00		3:00	3:00
3:30		3:30	3:30
4:00		4:00	4:00
4:30		4:30	4:30
5:00		5:00	5:00
5:30		5:30	5:30
6:00		6:00	6:00
6:30		6:30	6:30
7:00		7:00	7:00
7:30		7:30	7:30
8:00		8:00	8:00
8:30		8:30	8:30
9:00		9:00	9:00
9:30		9:30	9:30
10:00		10:00	10:00
10:30		10:30	10:30
11:00		11:00	11:00

Ready for tomorrow?	( )	( )	( )
ALARM			
CLOTHES			
GLASS OF WATER			
SAVERS PREP			
BEDTIME AFFIRMATIONS			

Wednesday		Thursday		Friday		Saturday	
S		S		S		S	
A		A		A		A	
V		V		V		V	
E		E		E		E	
R		R		R		R	
S		S		S		S	
◆		◆		◆		◆	
◆		◆		◆		◆	
5:00		5:00		5:00		5:00	
5:30		5:30		5:30		5:30	
6:00		6:00		6:00		6:00	
6:30		6:30		6:30		6:30	
7:00		7:00		7:00		7:00	
7:30		7:30		7:30		7:30	
8:00		8:00		8:00		8:00	
8:30		8:30		8:30		8:30	
9:00		9:00		9:00		9:00	
9:30		9:30		9:30		9:30	
10:00		10:00		10:00		10:00	
10:30		10:30		10:30		10:30	
11:00		11:00		11:00		11:00	
11:30		11:30		11:30		11:30	
12:00		12:00		12:00		12:00	
12:30		12:30		12:30		12:30	
1:00		1:00		1:00		1:00	
1:30		1:30		1:30		1:30	
2:00		2:00		2:00		2:00	
2:30		2:30		2:30		2:30	
3:00		3:00		3:00		3:00	
3:30		3:30		3:30		3:30	
4:00		4:00		4:00		4:00	
4:30		4:30		4:30		4:30	
5:00		5:00		5:00		5:00	
5:30		5:30		5:30		5:30	
6:00		6:00		6:00		6:00	
6:30		6:30		6:30		6:30	
7:00		7:00		7:00		7:00	
7:30		7:30		7:30		7:30	
8:00		8:00		8:00		8:00	
8:30		8:30		8:30		8:30	
9:00		9:00		9:00		9:00	
9:30		9:30		9:30		9:30	
10:00		10:00		10:00		10:00	
10:30		10:30		10:30		10:30	
11:00		11:00		11:00		11:00	
	( )		( )		( )		( )

Week of:	Sunday	Monday	Tuesday
This Week's Goal	S	S	S
	A	A	A
	V	V	V
	E	E	E
	R	R	R
	S	S	S
Intention for the Day	◆	◆	◆
Grateful for ...	◆	◆	◆

Everything you've ever wanted is on the other side of fear.

–GEORGE ADDAIR

TO-DO LIST	Sunday	Monday	Tuesday
Highest Priority	5:00	5:00	5:00
	5:30	5:30	5:30
	6:00	6:00	6:00
	6:30	6:30	6:30
	7:00	7:00	7:00
	7:30	7:30	7:30
	8:00	8:00	8:00
	8:30	8:30	8:30
	9:00	9:00	9:00
	9:30	9:30	9:30
	10:00	10:00	10:00
	10:30	10:30	10:30
	11:00	11:00	11:00
	11:30	11:30	11:30
	12:00	12:00	12:00
	12:30	12:30	12:30
	1:00	1:00	1:00
Definite Priority	1:30	1:30	1:30
	2:00	2:00	2:00
	2:30	2:30	2:30
	3:00	3:00	3:00
	3:30	3:30	3:30
	4:00	4:00	4:00
Lowest Priority	4:30	4:30	4:30
	5:00	5:00	5:00
	5:30	5:30	5:30
	6:00	6:00	6:00
	6:30	6:30	6:30
	7:00	7:00	7:00
	7:30	7:30	7:30
Habit to Work on This Week	8:00	8:00	8:00
	8:30	8:30	8:30
	9:00	9:00	9:00
	9:30	9:30	9:30
	10:00	10:00	10:00
	10:30	10:30	10:30
	11:00	11:00	11:00

Ready for tomorrow?	( )	( )	( )
ALARM			
CLOTHES			
GLASS OF WATER			
SAVERS PREP			
BEDTIME AFFIRMATIONS			

Wednesday		Thursday		Friday		Saturday	
S		S		S		S	
A		A		A		A	
V		V		V		V	
E		E		E		E	
R		R		R		R	
S		S		S		S	
◆		◆		◆		◆	
◆		◆		◆		◆	
5:00		5:00		5:00		5:00	
5:30		5:30		5:30		5:30	
6:00		6:00		6:00		6:00	
6:30		6:30		6:30		6:30	
7:00		7:00		7:00		7:00	
7:30		7:30		7:30		7:30	
8:00		8:00		8:00		8:00	
8:30		8:30		8:30		8:30	
9:00		9:00		9:00		9:00	
9:30		9:30		9:30		9:30	
10:00		10:00		10:00		10:00	
10:30		10:30		10:30		10:30	
11:00		11:00		11:00		11:00	
11:30		11:30		11:30		11:30	
12:00		12:00		12:00		12:00	
12:30		12:30		12:30		12:30	
1:00		1:00		1:00		1:00	
1:30		1:30		1:30		1:30	
2:00		2:00		2:00		2:00	
2:30		2:30		2:30		2:30	
3:00		3:00		3:00		3:00	
3:30		3:30		3:30		3:30	
4:00		4:00		4:00		4:00	
4:30		4:30		4:30		4:30	
5:00		5:00		5:00		5:00	
5:30		5:30		5:30		5:30	
6:00		6:00		6:00		6:00	
6:30		6:30		6:30		6:30	
7:00		7:00		7:00		7:00	
7:30		7:30		7:30		7:30	
8:00		8:00		8:00		8:00	
8:30		8:30		8:30		8:30	
9:00		9:00		9:00		9:00	
9:30		9:30		9:30		9:30	
10:00		10:00		10:00		10:00	
10:30		10:30		10:30		10:30	
11:00		11:00		11:00		11:00	
( )		( )		( )		( )	

Week of:	Sunday	Monday	Tuesday
This Week's Goal	S	S	S
	A	A	A
	V	V	V
	E	E	E
	R	R	R
	S	S	S
Intention for the Day	◆	◆	◆
Grateful for ...	◆	◆	◆

A year from now you may wish you had started today.

—KAREN LAMB

	Sunday	Monday	Tuesday
TO-DO LIST			
Highest Priority	5:00	5:00	5:00
	5:30	5:30	5:30
	6:00	6:00	6:00
	6:30	6:30	6:30
	7:00	7:00	7:00
	7:30	7:30	7:30
	8:00	8:00	8:00
	8:30	8:30	8:30
	9:00	9:00	9:00
	9:30	9:30	9:30
	10:00	10:00	10:00
	10:30	10:30	10:30
	11:00	11:00	11:00
	11:30	11:30	11:30
	12:00	12:00	12:00
	12:30	12:30	12:30
	1:00	1:00	1:00
Definite Priority	1:30	1:30	1:30
	2:00	2:00	2:00
	2:30	2:30	2:30
	3:00	3:00	3:00
	3:30	3:30	3:30
	4:00	4:00	4:00
Lowest Priority	4:30	4:30	4:30
	5:00	5:00	5:00
	5:30	5:30	5:30
	6:00	6:00	6:00
	6:30	6:30	6:30
	7:00	7:00	7:00
	7:30	7:30	7:30
Habit to Work on This Week	8:00	8:00	8:00
	8:30	8:30	8:30
	9:00	9:00	9:00
	9:30	9:30	9:30
	10:00	10:00	10:00
	10:30	10:30	10:30
	11:00	11:00	11:00

Ready for tomorrow?	( )	( )	( )
ALARM			
CLOTHES			
GLASS OF WATER			
SAVERS PREP			
BEDTIME AFFIRMATIONS			

Wednesday		Thursday		Friday		Saturday	
S		S		S		S	
A		A		A		A	
V		V		V		V	
E		E		E		E	
R		R		R		R	
S		S		S		S	
◆		◆		◆		◆	
◆		◆		◆		◆	
5:00		5:00		5:00		5:00	
5:30		5:30		5:30		5:30	
6:00		6:00		6:00		6:00	
6:30		6:30		6:30		6:30	
7:00		7:00		7:00		7:00	
7:30		7:30		7:30		7:30	
8:00		8:00		8:00		8:00	
8:30		8:30		8:30		8:30	
9:00		9:00		9:00		9:00	
9:30		9:30		9:30		9:30	
10:00		10:00		10:00		10:00	
10:30		10:30		10:30		10:30	
11:00		11:00		11:00		11:00	
11:30		11:30		11:30		11:30	
12:00		12:00		12:00		12:00	
12:30		12:30		12:30		12:30	
1:00		1:00		1:00		1:00	
1:30		1:30		1:30		1:30	
2:00		2:00		2:00		2:00	
2:30		2:30		2:30		2:30	
3:00		3:00		3:00		3:00	
3:30		3:30		3:30		3:30	
4:00		4:00		4:00		4:00	
4:30		4:30		4:30		4:30	
5:00		5:00		5:00		5:00	
5:30		5:30		5:30		5:30	
6:00		6:00		6:00		6:00	
6:30		6:30		6:30		6:30	
7:00		7:00		7:00		7:00	
7:30		7:30		7:30		7:30	
8:00		8:00		8:00		8:00	
8:30		8:30		8:30		8:30	
9:00		9:00		9:00		9:00	
9:30		9:30		9:30		9:30	
10:00		10:00		10:00		10:00	
10:30		10:30		10:30		10:30	
11:00		11:00		11:00		11:00	
	(　)		(　)		(　)		(　)

Week of:	Sunday	Monday	Tuesday
This Week's Goal	S	S	S
	A	A	A
	V	V	V
	E	E	E
	R	R	R
	S	S	S
Intention for the Day	◆	◆	◆
Grateful for ...	◆	◆	◆

It is never too late to be what you might have been.

—GEORGE ELIOT

TO-DO LIST

Highest Priority

Definite Priority

Lowest Priority

Habit to Work on This Week

Time	Sunday	Monday	Tuesday
5:00		5:00	5:00
5:30		5:30	5:30
6:00		6:00	6:00
6:30		6:30	6:30
7:00		7:00	7:00
7:30		7:30	7:30
8:00		8:00	8:00
8:30		8:30	8:30
9:00		9:00	9:00
9:30		9:30	9:30
10:00		10:00	10:00
10:30		10:30	10:30
11:00		11:00	11:00
11:30		11:30	11:30
12:00		12:00	12:00
12:30		12:30	12:30
1:00		1:00	1:00
1:30		1:30	1:30
2:00		2:00	2:00
2:30		2:30	2:30
3:00		3:00	3:00
3:30		3:30	3:30
4:00		4:00	4:00
4:30		4:30	4:30
5:00		5:00	5:00
5:30		5:30	5:30
6:00		6:00	6:00
6:30		6:30	6:30
7:00		7:00	7:00
7:30		7:30	7:30
8:00		8:00	8:00
8:30		8:30	8:30
9:00		9:00	9:00
9:30		9:30	9:30
10:00		10:00	10:00
10:30		10:30	10:30
11:00		11:00	11:00

Ready for tomorrow?	( )	( )	( )
ALARM			
CLOTHES			
GLASS OF WATER			
SAVERS PREP			
BEDTIME AFFIRMATIONS			

Wednesday		Thursday		Friday		Saturday	
S		S		S		S	
A		A		A		A	
V		V		V		V	
E		E		E		E	
R		R		R		R	
S		S		S		S	
◆		◆		◆		◆	
◆		◆		◆		◆	
5:00		5:00		5:00		5:00	
5:30		5:30		5:30		5:30	
6:00		6:00		6:00		6:00	
6:30		6:30		6:30		6:30	
7:00		7:00		7:00		7:00	
7:30		7:30		7:30		7:30	
8:00		8:00		8:00		8:00	
8:30		8:30		8:30		8:30	
9:00		9:00		9:00		9:00	
9:30		9:30		9:30		9:30	
10:00		10:00		10:00		10:00	
10:30		10:30		10:30		10:30	
11:00		11:00		11:00		11:00	
11:30		11:30		11:30		11:30	
12:00		12:00		12:00		12:00	
12:30		12:30		12:30		12:30	
1:00		1:00		1:00		1:00	
1:30		1:30		1:30		1:30	
2:00		2:00		2:00		2:00	
2:30		2:30		2:30		2:30	
3:00		3:00		3:00		3:00	
3:30		3:30		3:30		3:30	
4:00		4:00		4:00		4:00	
4:30		4:30		4:30		4:30	
5:00		5:00		5:00		5:00	
5:30		5:30		5:30		5:30	
6:00		6:00		6:00		6:00	
6:30		6:30		6:30		6:30	
7:00		7:00		7:00		7:00	
7:30		7:30		7:30		7:30	
8:00		8:00		8:00		8:00	
8:30		8:30		8:30		8:30	
9:00		9:00		9:00		9:00	
9:30		9:30		9:30		9:30	
10:00		10:00		10:00		10:00	
10:30		10:30		10:30		10:30	
11:00		11:00		11:00		11:00	
	( )		( )		( )		( )

Week of:	Sunday	Monday	Tuesday
This Week's Goal	S	S	S
	A	A	A
	V	V	V
	E	E	E
	R	R	R
	S	S	S
Intention for the Day	◆	◆	◆
Grateful for ...	◆	◆	◆

What we fear doing most is usually what we most need to do.

—TIM FERRISS

TO-DO LIST
Highest Priority
Definite Priority
Lowest Priority
Habit to Work on This Week

Time	Sunday	Monday	Tuesday
5:00		5:00	5:00
5:30		5:30	5:30
6:00		6:00	6:00
6:30		6:30	6:30
7:00		7:00	7:00
7:30		7:30	7:30
8:00		8:00	8:00
8:30		8:30	8:30
9:00		9:00	9:00
9:30		9:30	9:30
10:00		10:00	10:00
10:30		10:30	10:30
11:00		11:00	11:00
11:30		11:30	11:30
12:00		12:00	12:00
12:30		12:30	12:30
1:00		1:00	1:00
1:30		1:30	1:30
2:00		2:00	2:00
2:30		2:30	2:30
3:00		3:00	3:00
3:30		3:30	3:30
4:00		4:00	4:00
4:30		4:30	4:30
5:00		5:00	5:00
5:30		5:30	5:30
6:00		6:00	6:00
6:30		6:30	6:30
7:00		7:00	7:00
7:30		7:30	7:30
8:00		8:00	8:00
8:30		8:30	8:30
9:00		9:00	9:00
9:30		9:30	9:30
10:00		10:00	10:00
10:30		10:30	10:30
11:00		11:00	11:00

Ready for tomorrow?	( )	( )	( )
ALARM			
CLOTHES			
GLASS OF WATER			
SAVERS PREP			
BEDTIME AFFIRMATIONS			

Wednesday		Thursday		Friday		Saturday	
S		S		S		S	
A		A		A		A	
V		V		V		V	
E		E		E		E	
R		R		R		R	
S		S		S		S	
◆		◆		◆		◆	
◆		◆		◆		◆	
5:00		5:00		5:00		5:00	
5:30		5:30		5:30		5:30	
6:00		6:00		6:00		6:00	
6:30		6:30		6:30		6:30	
7:00		7:00		7:00		7:00	
7:30		7:30		7:30		7:30	
8:00		8:00		8:00		8:00	
8:30		8:30		8:30		8:30	
9:00		9:00		9:00		9:00	
9:30		9:30		9:30		9:30	
10:00		10:00		10:00		10:00	
10:30		10:30		10:30		10:30	
11:00		11:00		11:00		11:00	
11:30		11:30		11:30		11:30	
12:00		12:00		12:00		12:00	
12:30		12:30		12:30		12:30	
1:00		1:00		1:00		1:00	
1:30		1:30		1:30		1:30	
2:00		2:00		2:00		2:00	
2:30		2:30		2:30		2:30	
3:00		3:00		3:00		3:00	
3:30		3:30		3:30		3:30	
4:00		4:00		4:00		4:00	
4:30		4:30		4:30		4:30	
5:00		5:00		5:00		5:00	
5:30		5:30		5:30		5:30	
6:00		6:00		6:00		6:00	
6:30		6:30		6:30		6:30	
7:00		7:00		7:00		7:00	
7:30		7:30		7:30		7:30	
8:00		8:00		8:00		8:00	
8:30		8:30		8:30		8:30	
9:00		9:00		9:00		9:00	
9:30		9:30		9:30		9:30	
10:00		10:00		10:00		10:00	
10:30		10:30		10:30		10:30	
11:00		11:00		11:00		11:00	
	( )		( )		( )		( )

MONTHLY REFLECTION

··

Write 5 things you accomplished this month:

1.

2.

3.

4.

5.

QUESTIONS

1) What did I learn about myself this month?

2) What tasks are left over from this month that are lingering and need to get done?

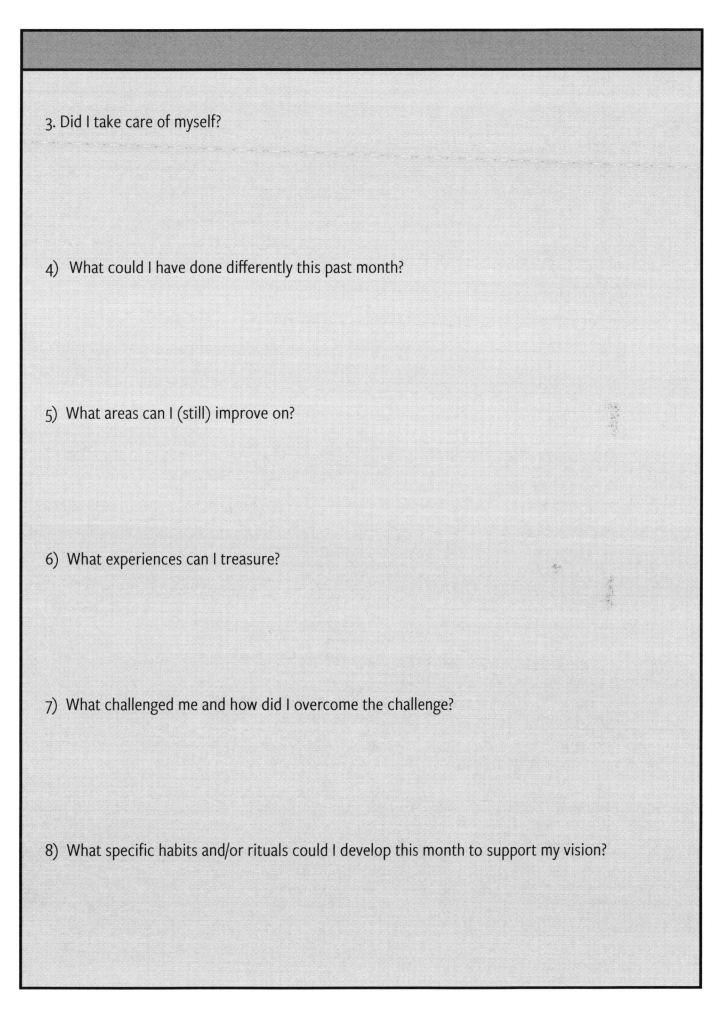

3. Did I take care of myself?

4) What could I have done differently this past month?

5) What areas can I (still) improve on?

6) What experiences can I treasure?

7) What challenged me and how did I overcome the challenge?

8) What specific habits and/or rituals could I develop this month to support my vision?

MONTH OF:	SUNDAY	MONDAY	TUESDAY
This Month's Goal			
Important Events or Reminders to Transfer to My Phone			
1.			
2.			
3.			
4.			
5.			
6.			
7.			
8.			
9.			
10.			

PROJECT NAME	TEAM PLAYERS	IMPORTANT DATES	DEADLINES
1.			
2.			
3.			
4.			

WEDNESDAY	THURSDAY	FRIDAY	SATURDAY

BRAINSTORM

Week of:	Sunday	Monday	Tuesday
This Week's Goal	S	S	S
	A	A	A
	V	V	V
	E	E	E
	R	R	R
	S	S	S
Intention for the Day	◆	◆	◆
Grateful for ...	◆	◆	◆

The more I want to get something done, the less I call it work.

—RICHARD BACH

TO-DO LIST

Highest Priority

Definite Priority

Lowest Priority

Habit to Work on This Week

Time	Sunday	Time	Monday	Time	Tuesday
5:00		5:00		5:00	
5:30		5:30		5:30	
6:00		6:00		6:00	
6:30		6:30		6:30	
7:00		7:00		7:00	
7:30		7:30		7:30	
8:00		8:00		8:00	
8:30		8:30		8:30	
9:00		9:00		9:00	
9:30		9:30		9:30	
10:00		10:00		10:00	
10:30		10:30		10:30	
11:00		11:00		11:00	
11:30		11:30		11:30	
12:00		12:00		12:00	
12:30		12:30		12:30	
1:00		1:00		1:00	
1:30		1:30		1:30	
2:00		2:00		2:00	
2:30		2:30		2:30	
3:00		3:00		3:00	
3:30		3:30		3:30	
4:00		4:00		4:00	
4:30		4:30		4:30	
5:00		5:00		5:00	
5:30		5:30		5:30	
6:00		6:00		6:00	
6:30		6:30		6:30	
7:00		7:00		7:00	
7:30		7:30		7:30	
8:00		8:00		8:00	
8:30		8:30		8:30	
9:00		9:00		9:00	
9:30		9:30		9:30	
10:00		10:00		10:00	
10:30		10:30		10:30	
11:00		11:00		11:00	

Ready for tomorrow?	( )	( )	( )
ALARM			
CLOTHES			
GLASS OF WATER			
SAVERS PREP			
BEDTIME AFFIRMATIONS			

Wednesday	Thursday	Friday	Saturday
S	S	S	S
A	A	A	A
V	V	V	V
E	E	E	E
R	R	R	R
S	S	S	S
◆	◆	◆	◆
◆	◆	◆	◆

Wednesday		Thursday		Friday		Saturday	
5:00		5:00		5:00		5:00	
5:30		5:30		5:30		5:30	
6:00		6:00		6:00		6:00	
6:30		6:30		6:30		6:30	
7:00		7:00		7:00		7:00	
7:30		7:30		7:30		7:30	
8:00		8:00		8:00		8:00	
8:30		8:30		8:30		8:30	
9:00		9:00		9:00		9:00	
9:30		9:30		9:30		9:30	
10:00		10:00		10:00		10:00	
10:30		10:30		10:30		10:30	
11:00		11:00		11:00		11:00	
11:30		11:30		11:30		11:30	
12:00		12:00		12:00		12:00	
12:30		12:30		12:30		12:30	
1:00		1:00		1:00		1:00	
1:30		1:30		1:30		1:30	
2:00		2:00		2:00		2:00	
2:30		2:30		2:30		2:30	
3:00		3:00		3:00		3:00	
3:30		3:30		3:30		3:30	
4:00		4:00		4:00		4:00	
4:30		4:30		4:30		4:30	
5:00		5:00		5:00		5:00	
5:30		5:30		5:30		5:30	
6:00		6:00		6:00		6:00	
6:30		6:30		6:30		6:30	
7:00		7:00		7:00		7:00	
7:30		7:30		7:30		7:30	
8:00		8:00		8:00		8:00	
8:30		8:30		8:30		8:30	
9:00		9:00		9:00		9:00	
9:30		9:30		9:30		9:30	
10:00		10:00		10:00		10:00	
10:30		10:30		10:30		10:30	
11:00		11:00		11:00		11:00	
( )		( )		( )		( )	

Week of:	Sunday		Monday		Tuesday	
This Week's Goal	S		S		S	
	A		A		A	
	V		V		V	
	E		E		E	
	R		R		R	
	S		S		S	
Intention for the Day	◆		◆		◆	
Grateful for ...	◆		◆		◆	

The best way to predict your future is to create it.

–ABRAHAM LINCOLN

	Sunday	Monday	Tuesday
	5:00	5:00	5:00
	5:30	5:30	5:30
	6:00	6:00	6:00
	6:30	6:30	6:30
	7:00	7:00	7:00
	7:30	7:30	7:30
	8:00	8:00	8:00
	8:30	8:30	8:30
	9:00	9:00	9:00
	9:30	9:30	9:30
TO-DO LIST	10:00	10:00	10:00
Highest Priority	10:30	10:30	10:30
	11:00	11:00	11:00
	11:30	11:30	11:30
	12:00	12:00	12:00
	12:30	12:30	12:30
	1:00	1:00	1:00
Definite Priority	1:30	1:30	1:30
	2:00	2:00	2:00
	2:30	2:30	2:30
	3:00	3:00	3:00
	3:30	3:30	3:30
	4:00	4:00	4:00
Lowest Priority	4:30	4:30	4:30
	5:00	5:00	5:00
	5:30	5:30	5:30
	6:00	6:00	6:00
	6:30	6:30	6:30
	7:00	7:00	7:00
	7:30	7:30	7:30
Habit to Work on This Week	8:00	8:00	8:00
	8:30	8:30	8:30
	9:00	9:00	9:00
	9:30	9:30	9:30
	10:00	10:00	10:00
	10:30	10:30	10:30
	11:00	11:00	11:00

Ready for tomorrow?	( )	( )	( )
ALARM			
CLOTHES			
GLASS OF WATER			
SAVERS PREP			
BEDTIME AFFIRMATIONS			

Wednesday		Thursday		Friday		Saturday	
S		S		S		S	
A		A		A		A	
V		V		V		V	
E		E		E		E	
R		R		R		R	
S		S		S		S	
◆		◆		◆		◆	
◆		◆		◆		◆	
5:00		5:00		5:00		5:00	
5:30		5:30		5:30		5:30	
6:00		6:00		6:00		6:00	
6:30		6:30		6:30		6:30	
7:00		7:00		7:00		7:00	
7:30		7:30		7:30		7:30	
8:00		8:00		8:00		8:00	
8:30		8:30		8:30		8:30	
9:00		9:00		9:00		9:00	
9:30		9:30		9:30		9:30	
10:00		10:00		10:00		10:00	
10:30		10:30		10:30		10:30	
11:00		11:00		11:00		11:00	
11:30		11:30		11:30		11:30	
12:00		12:00		12:00		12:00	
12:30		12:30		12:30		12:30	
1:00		1:00		1:00		1:00	
1:30		1:30		1:30		1:30	
2:00		2:00		2:00		2:00	
2:30		2:30		2:30		2:30	
3:00		3:00		3:00		3:00	
3:30		3:30		3:30		3:30	
4:00		4:00		4:00		4:00	
4:30		4:30		4:30		4:30	
5:00		5:00		5:00		5:00	
5:30		5:30		5:30		5:30	
6:00		6:00		6:00		6:00	
6:30		6:30		6:30		6:30	
7:00		7:00		7:00		7:00	
7:30		7:30		7:30		7:30	
8:00		8:00		8:00		8:00	
8:30		8:30		8:30		8:30	
9:00		9:00		9:00		9:00	
9:30		9:30		9:30		9:30	
10:00		10:00		10:00		10:00	
10:30		10:30		10:30		10:30	
11:00		11:00		11:00		11:00	
	( )		( )		( )		( )

Week of:	Sunday		Monday		Tuesday	
This Week's Goal	S		S		S	
	A		A		A	
	V		V		V	
	E		E		E	
	R		R		R	
	S		S		S	
Intention for the Day	◆		◆		◆	
Grateful for ...	◆		◆		◆	

	Sunday	Monday	Tuesday
The dreamers are the saviors of the world. —JAMES ALLEN	5:00	5:00	5:00
	5:30	5:30	5:30
	6:00	6:00	6:00
	6:30	6:30	6:30
	7:00	7:00	7:00
	7:30	7:30	7:30
	8:00	8:00	8:00
	8:30	8:30	8:30
	9:00	9:00	9:00
	9:30	9:30	9:30
TO-DO LIST	10:00	10:00	10:00
Highest Priority	10:30	10:30	10:30
	11:00	11:00	11:00
	11:30	11:30	11:30
	12:00	12:00	12:00
	12:30	12:30	12:30
	1:00	1:00	1:00
Definite Priority	1:30	1:30	1:30
	2:00	2:00	2:00
	2:30	2:30	2:30
	3:00	3:00	3:00
	3:30	3:30	3:30
	4:00	4:00	4:00
Lowest Priority	4:30	4:30	4:30
	5:00	5:00	5:00
	5:30	5:30	5:30
	6:00	6:00	6:00
	6:30	6:30	6:30
	7:00	7:00	7:00
	7:30	7:30	7:30
Habit to Work on This Week	8:00	8:00	8:00
	8:30	8:30	8:30
	9:00	9:00	9:00
	9:30	9:30	9:30
	10:00	10:00	10:00
	10:30	10:30	10:30
	11:00	11:00	11:00

Ready for tomorrow?	( )	( )	( )
ALARM			
CLOTHES			
GLASS OF WATER			
SAVERS PREP			
BEDTIME AFFIRMATIONS			

Wednesday		Thursday		Friday		Saturday	
S		S		S		S	
A		A		A		A	
V		V		V		V	
E		E		E		E	
R		R		R		R	
S		S		S		S	
◆		◆		◆		◆	
◆		◆		◆		◆	
5:00		5:00		5:00		5:00	
5:30		5:30		5:30		5:30	
6:00		6:00		6:00		6:00	
6:30		6:30		6:30		6:30	
7:00		7:00		7:00		7:00	
7:30		7:30		7:30		7:30	
8:00		8:00		8:00		8:00	
8:30		8:30		8:30		8:30	
9:00		9:00		9:00		9:00	
9:30		9:30		9:30		9:30	
10:00		10:00		10:00		10:00	
10:30		10:30		10:30		10:30	
11:00		11:00		11:00		11:00	
11:30		11:30		11:30		11:30	
12:00		12:00		12:00		12:00	
12:30		12:30		12:30		12:30	
1:00		1:00		1:00		1:00	
1:30		1:30		1:30		1:30	
2:00		2:00		2:00		2:00	
2:30		2:30		2:30		2:30	
3:00		3:00		3:00		3:00	
3:30		3:30		3:30		3:30	
4:00		4:00		4:00		4:00	
4:30		4:30		4:30		4:30	
5:00		5:00		5:00		5:00	
5:30		5:30		5:30		5:30	
6:00		6:00		6:00		6:00	
6:30		6:30		6:30		6:30	
7:00		7:00		7:00		7:00	
7:30		7:30		7:30		7:30	
8:00		8:00		8:00		8:00	
8:30		8:30		8:30		8:30	
9:00		9:00		9:00		9:00	
9:30		9:30		9:30		9:30	
10:00		10:00		10:00		10:00	
10:30		10:30		10:30		10:30	
11:00		11:00		11:00		11:00	
	( )		( )		( )		( )

Week of:	Sunday		Monday		Tuesday	
This Week's Goal	S		S		S	
	A		A		A	
	V		V		V	
	E		E		E	
	R		R		R	
	S		S		S	
Intention for the Day	◆		◆		◆	
Grateful for ...	◆		◆		◆	

There are no short cuts to any place worth going.

—BEVERLY SILLS

	Sunday	Monday	Tuesday
TO-DO LIST	5:00	5:00	5:00
Highest Priority	5:30	5:30	5:30
	6:00	6:00	6:00
	6:30	6:30	6:30
	7:00	7:00	7:00
	7:30	7:30	7:30
	8:00	8:00	8:00
	8:30	8:30	8:30
	9:00	9:00	9:00
	9:30	9:30	9:30
	10:00	10:00	10:00
	10:30	10:30	10:30
	11:00	11:00	11:00
	11:30	11:30	11:30
	12:00	12:00	12:00
	12:30	12:30	12:30
	1:00	1:00	1:00
Definite Priority	1:30	1:30	1:30
	2:00	2:00	2:00
	2:30	2:30	2:30
	3:00	3:00	3:00
	3:30	3:30	3:30
	4:00	4:00	4:00
Lowest Priority	4:30	4:30	4:30
	5:00	5:00	5:00
	5:30	5:30	5:30
	6:00	6:00	6:00
	6:30	6:30	6:30
	7:00	7:00	7:00
	7:30	7:30	7:30
Habit to Work on This Week	8:00	8:00	8:00
	8:30	8:30	8:30
	9:00	9:00	9:00
	9:30	9:30	9:30
	10:00	10:00	10:00
	10:30	10:30	10:30
	11:00	11:00	11:00

Ready for tomorrow?	( )	( )	( )
ALARM			
CLOTHES			
GLASS OF WATER			
SAVERS PREP			
BEDTIME AFFIRMATIONS			

Wednesday		Thursday		Friday		Saturday	
S		S		S		S	
A		A		A		A	
V		V		V		V	
E		E		E		E	
R		R		R		R	
S		S		S		S	
◆		◆		◆		◆	
◆		◆		◆		◆	
5:00		5:00		5:00		5:00	
5:30		5:30		5:30		5:30	
6:00		6:00		6:00		6:00	
6:30		6:30		6:30		6:30	
7:00		7:00		7:00		7:00	
7:30		7:30		7:30		7:30	
8:00		8:00		8:00		8:00	
8:30		8:30		8:30		8:30	
9:00		9:00		9:00		9:00	
9:30		9:30		9:30		9:30	
10:00		10:00		10:00		10:00	
10:30		10:30		10:30		10:30	
11:00		11:00		11:00		11:00	
11:30		11:30		11:30		11:30	
12:00		12:00		12:00		12:00	
12:30		12:30		12:30		12:30	
1:00		1:00		1:00		1:00	
1:30		1:30		1:30		1:30	
2:00		2:00		2:00		2:00	
2:30		2:30		2:30		2:30	
3:00		3:00		3:00		3:00	
3:30		3:30		3:30		3:30	
4:00		4:00		4:00		4:00	
4:30		4:30		4:30		4:30	
5:00		5:00		5:00		5:00	
5:30		5:30		5:30		5:30	
6:00		6:00		6:00		6:00	
6:30		6:30		6:30		6:30	
7:00		7:00		7:00		7:00	
7:30		7:30		7:30		7:30	
8:00		8:00		8:00		8:00	
8:30		8:30		8:30		8:30	
9:00		9:00		9:00		9:00	
9:30		9:30		9:30		9:30	
10:00		10:00		10:00		10:00	
10:30		10:30		10:30		10:30	
11:00		11:00		11:00		11:00	
	( )		( )		( )		( )

Week of:	Sunday	Monday	Tuesday
This Week's Goal	S	S	S
	A	A	A
	V	V	V
	E	E	E
	R	R	R
	S	S	S
Intention for the Day	◆	◆	◆
Grateful for ...	◆	◆	◆

Very often a change of self is needed more than a change of scene.

—ARTHUR CHRISTOPHER BENSON

TO-DO LIST

Highest Priority

Definite Priority

Lowest Priority

Habit to Work on This Week

Sunday	Monday	Tuesday
5:00	5:00	5:00
5:30	5:30	5:30
6:00	6:00	6:00
6:30	6:30	6:30
7:00	7:00	7:00
7:30	7:30	7:30
8:00	8:00	8:00
8:30	8:30	8:30
9:00	9:00	9:00
9:30	9:30	9:30
10:00	10:00	10:00
10:30	10:30	10:30
11:00	11:00	11:00
11:30	11:30	11:30
12:00	12:00	12:00
12:30	12:30	12:30
1:00	1:00	1:00
1:30	1:30	1:30
2:00	2:00	2:00
2:30	2:30	2:30
3:00	3:00	3:00
3:30	3:30	3:30
4:00	4:00	4:00
4:30	4:30	4:30
5:00	5:00	5:00
5:30	5:30	5:30
6:00	6:00	6:00
6:30	6:30	6:30
7:00	7:00	7:00
7:30	7:30	7:30
8:00	8:00	8:00
8:30	8:30	8:30
9:00	9:00	9:00
9:30	9:30	9:30
10:00	10:00	10:00
10:30	10:30	10:30
11:00	11:00	11:00

Ready for tomorrow?	( )	( )	( )
ALARM			
CLOTHES			
GLASS OF WATER			
SAVERS PREP			
BEDTIME AFFIRMATIONS			

Wednesday	Thursday	Friday	Saturday
S	S	S	S
A	A	A	A
V	V	V	V
E	E	E	E
R	R	R	R
S	S	S	S
◆	◆	◆	◆
◆	◆	◆	◆

Wednesday	Thursday	Friday	Saturday
5:00	5:00	5:00	5:00
5:30	5:30	5:30	5:30
6:00	6:00	6:00	6:00
6:30	6:30	6:30	6:30
7:00	7:00	7:00	7:00
7:30	7:30	7:30	7:30
8:00	8:00	8:00	8:00
8:30	8:30	8:30	8:30
9:00	9:00	9:00	9:00
9:30	9:30	9:30	9:30
10:00	10:00	10:00	10:00
10:30	10:30	10:30	10:30
11:00	11:00	11:00	11:00
11:30	11:30	11:30	11:30
12:00	12:00	12:00	12:00
12:30	12:30	12:30	12:30
1:00	1:00	1:00	1:00
1:30	1:30	1:30	1:30
2:00	2:00	2:00	2:00
2:30	2:30	2:30	2:30
3:00	3:00	3:00	3:00
3:30	3:30	3:30	3:30
4:00	4:00	4:00	4:00
4:30	4:30	4:30	4:30
5:00	5:00	5:00	5:00
5:30	5:30	5:30	5:30
6:00	6:00	6:00	6:00
6:30	6:30	6:30	6:30
7:00	7:00	7:00	7:00
7:30	7:30	7:30	7:30
8:00	8:00	8:00	8:00
8:30	8:30	8:30	8:30
9:00	9:00	9:00	9:00
9:30	9:30	9:30	9:30
10:00	10:00	10:00	10:00
10:30	10:30	10:30	10:30
11:00	11:00	11:00	11:00

( )	( )	( )	( )

MONTHLY REFLECTION

....

Write 5 things you accomplished this month:

1.

2.

3.

4.

5.

QUESTIONS

1) What did I learn about myself this month?

2) What tasks are left over from this month that are lingering and need to get done?

3. Did I take care of myself?

4) What could I have done differently this past month?

5) What areas can I (still) improve on?

6) What experiences can I treasure?

7) What challenged me and how did I overcome the challenge?

8) What specific habits and/or rituals could I develop this month to support my vision?

REFERENCES

Sample Affirmations

- I am just as worthy, deserving, and capable of achieving personal and academic success as any other person on earth, and I will prove that today with my actions.

- I am becoming healthier each day because I am committed to making healthy choices for my body and my mind every day.

- Where I *am* is a result of who I *was*, but where I go depends entirely on who I *choose to be* starting today.

- I choose to take 100% responsibility for my own success, because my success depends on my actions and decisions each day.

- I am a hardworking, intelligent student and I committed to excelling in my major and career.

- I am fully committed to dedicating 30–60 minutes to do my Miracle Morning and the Life S.A.V.E.R.S. so that I can continue to become the person I need to be to create everything I want for my life.

- I am fully committed to replace my complaints with words of gratitude, because even in the midst of difficulty, gratitude will bring more appreciation to the present moment than complaining.

- I am grateful for all my wins, and most especially for all my "losses", because each of those experiences hold the knowledge of how I can further improve as a student and as an individual.

- I focus on learning new things and improving my self-awareness daily, and I commit to reading or rereading at least one book to help that effort every month.

- By asking the right questions, I continue to learn more about myself so that I will create a clearer picture of my overall vision.

- I am committed to constant and never-ending improvement in the tasks necessary for the day-to-day functioning of a college student.

Sample Journal Questions

- What is the one thing I want to accomplish today?

- Where can I find more time in my schedule? How might I be able to do that?

- What does a Level 10 post-graduation life look like to me?

- What are my biggest hopes and dreams?

- What is my life's passion?

- What do I love to do?

- What am I best at?

- What problem can I solve?

- How can I add value to the world?

- What dream job do I want to have?

- How might I go about creating a life that I would be happy to call my reality?

- What realization have I had recently?

- How can I be more proactive about my life and my future today?

- What's working that I should *keep doing* (or do more of)?

- What do I need to *start doing* to accelerate results?

- What do I need to *stop doing* immediately that's holding me back from going to the next level?

- What is one habit I can practice to improve health? Productivity? Clarity?

- How will I overcome the obstacles that come my way today?

- What can I feel joy about today?

- What can I feel grateful for this morning?

- How have I improved in these last few weeks?

- Where do I see myself in a year? Two years? Five years?

- What are some changes I'd like to make to my Miracle Morning?

Apps for Meditation

- Headspace
- Calm
- Omvana
- Simply Being
- Insight Timer

BOOKS

On Mindset

- *The Art of Exceptional Living* by Jim Rohn

- *The One Thing: The Surprisingly Simple Truth Behind Extraordinary Results* by Gary Keller and Jay Papasan

- *The 7 Habits of Highly Effective People: Powerful Lessons in Personal Change* by Stephen R. Covey

- *Mastery* by Robert Greene

- *The 4-Hour Workweek: Escape 9–5, Live Anywhere, and Join the New Rich* by Tim Ferriss

- *The Game of Life and How to Play It* by Florence Scovel Shinn

- *The Compound Effect* by Darren Hardy

- *Man's Search for Meaning* by Viktor Frankl

- *Taking Life Head On: How to Love the Life You Have While You Create the Life of Your Dreams* by Hal Elrod

- *Think and Grow Rich* by Napoleon Hill

- *Vision to Reality: How Short Term Massive Action Equals Long Term Maximum Results* by Honorée Corder

- *Finding Your Element: How to Discover Your Talents and Passions and Transform Your Life* by Sir Ken Robinson and Lou Aronica

- *You Are a Badass: How to Stop Doubting Your Greatness and Start Living an Awesome Life* by Jen Sincero

ON DEVELOPING YOUR MONEY MINDSET

- *Think and Grow Rich* by Napoleon Hill

- *The Richest Man in Babylon* by George Samuel Clason

- *Rich Dad Poor Dad* by Robert Kiyosaki

- *Secrets of the Millionaire Mind: Mastering the Inner Game of Wealth* by T. Harv Ecker

- *The Total Money Makeover: A Proven Plan for Financial Fitness* by Dave Ramsey

- *The Millionaire Fastlane: Crack the Code to Wealth and Live Rich for a Lifetime* by MJ DeMarco

- *Profit First: A Simple System to Transform Any Business from a Cash-Eating Monster to a Money-Making Machine* by Mike Michalowicz

- *MONEY: Master the Game: 7 Simple Steps to Financial Freedom* by Tony Robbins

- *Magic Money 3-Book Series* by Holly Alexander

ABOUT THE AUTHORS

HAL ELROD is one of the highest-rated keynote speakers in America, as evidenced by his average of 9.7 out of 10.0 rating across multiple Entrepreneur Organization (EO) chapters. However, he's still best known as the author of what is now being widely regarded as one of the most life-changing books ever written (with 1,500+ five-star reviews on Amazon), *The Miracle Morning: The Not-So-Obvious Secret Guaranteed to Transform Your Life (Before 8AM)*, which has been translated into 21 languages and is a best seller around the world.

The seed for Hal's life's work was planted at age 20 when Hal was found dead at the scene of a horrific car accident. Hit head-on by a drunk driver at 70 miles per hour, he broke 11 bones, died for six minutes, and suffered permanent brain damage. After six days in a coma, he woke to face his unimaginable reality—which included being told by doctors that he would never walk again. Defying the logic of doctors, and proving that all of us are capable of overcoming even seemingly insurmountable adversity to achieve anything we set our minds to, Hal went on not only to walk again, but to run a 52-mile ultramarathon and become a hall of fame business achiever, international best-selling author, keynote speaker, and host of the *Achieve Your Goals* podcast on iTunes.

Most importantly, Hal is beyond grateful to now be married to the woman of his dreams and a father of two, sharing his life with his wife and children in Austin, Texas.

For more information on Hal's keynote speaking, live events, coaching, books, and the soon-to-be released *Miracle Morning Movie* (documentary), visit www.HalElrod.com.

NATALIE JANJI is a graduate of Loyola Marymount University and has a bachelor's degree in chemistry. After reading *The Miracle Morning* book, she became aware of her growing passion to help college students live to their full potential. Natalie is currently a speaker, coach, and author ready to set the world on fire (figuratively). You can find out more about her at NatalieJanji.com. Connect with her personally on Facebook.com/natalie.janji, **The Miracle Morning for College Students** Facebook page, Instagram @nat_janji, Twitter @janji_natalie, and LinkedIn, where you will find motivation, advice, and any help you would need when it comes to success in college and life.

HONORÉE CORDER is the author of dozens of books, including *You Must Write a Book, Vision to Reality, The Prosperous Writer* book series, *Business Dating, The Successful Single Mom* book series, *If Divorce is a Game, These are the Rules*, and *The Divorced Phoenix*. She is also Hal Elrod's business partner in *The Miracle Morning* book series. Honorée coaches business professionals, writers, and aspiring non-fiction authors who want to publish their books to bestseller status, create a platform, and develop multiple streams of income. She also does all sorts of other magical things, and her badassery is legendary. You can find out more at HonoreeCorder.com.

Made in the USA
San Bernardino, CA
29 May 2020

72468152R00120